G000042863

Yorkshire Dales: limestone country

Limestone pavement at Southerscales Scar, Ingleborough

Stalactites and stalagmites in Ease Gill Caverns

Yorkshire Dales: limestone country

Tony Waltham

Constable London

First published in Great Britain as *Caves, Crags and Gorges* 1984
by Constable and Company Ltd
10 Orange Street London WC2H 7EG
Copyright © 1984 Tony Waltham
Revised as *Yorkshire Dales: limestone country* 1987
Copyright © 1987 Tony Waltham
ISBN 0 09 467610 0
Set in Times New Roman 9pt by
Inforum Ltd Portsmouth
Printed and bound in Great Britain
by The Bath Press, Avon

Contents

Contents

Illustrations

Illustrations

Maps

Acknowledgements

The descriptions in this guide are the result of many years spent and enjoyed in the Yorkshire Dales, both above and below ground. The cave explorations have only been possible in the company of many friends, to whom the author will always be grateful, especially when time was taken out for photography. Similarly the author was accompanied by his wife on many of the walks, and is also grateful to Harry Long for so many valuable discussions.

All the maps have been drawn by the author, with information abstracted from many published sources. Photographs are by the author except where otherwise credited.

T.W.
1986

Rising and sinking stream at Runscar, Ribbleshead

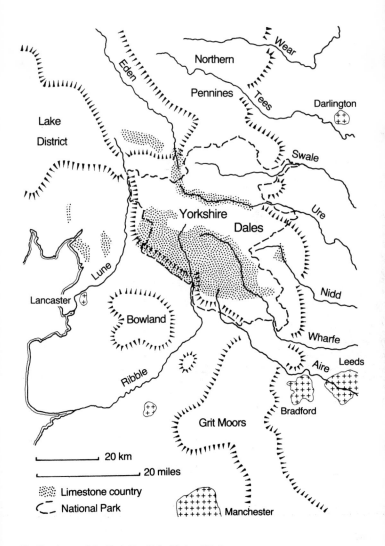

The Pennines and the Yorkshire Dales National Park

Introduction

Cut into the heart of the Pennines, the Yorkshire Dales provide some of the finest landscapes in Britain. The character of the Dales is dictated by the limestone which is the most conspicuous and dominating rock unit in the whole Pennines. It not only determines the nature of the land-forms but also imposes itself on the detail and texture of the countryside as established by man. From towering cliff and plummeting cave to drystone wall and grazing sheep: all are reflections of the limestone. The Yorkshire Dales are limestone country, and consequently they have a character, a beauty and an appeal which is irreplaceable and unforgettable.

The finest of the Dales landscapes are incorporated in the Yorkshire Dales National Park, and in fact were a major factor behind the creation of the Park. The geological structure of the Pennines means that the most spectacular landscapes are in a belt across the southern part of the National Park, centred on the well-known limestone areas of Ingleborough and Malham. There the Carboniferous limestone sequence generally known as the Great Scar is the dominant feature of the landscape. This one rock, the Great Scar Limestone, provides the backbone to this guide-book. Nearly all the sites in the following pages are on this rock in the southern half of the National Park; a few are on areas of the same limestone just outside the Park, and some are on other comparable limestones in the northern sector of the Dales.

Limestone country has its own special features, and therefore needs its own distinctive style of guide-book. The unique feature of limestone is that its land-forms are developed both above and below ground. On the surface, the bare white crags, the dry valleys, the deep gorges and the expanses of limestone pavement provide splendid walking country with a feast of landscape variety. The best of the limestone walks in the Dales are followed in this guide, with insights into the geology and geomorphology, and also some glimpses of the history of the landscapes. And then underground there are the caves which make limestone country unique. Many of these require considerable effort to explore, and are the preserve of the experienced and fully equipped caver, but they can also provide some fascinating armchair caving. This guide features a few of the major cave systems, but it also describes the show caves and the best of the uncommercialised caves which can be safely explored without full caving equipment.

Not all Britain's limestone country is in the Yorkshire Dales. The same Carboniferous limestone provides the spectacular scenery and well-known caves of the Peak District in Derbyshire, the Mendip Hills south of Bristol and some areas in both North and South Wales. The predecessor to this book was *Caves, Crags and Gorges*, a guide which delved into all the limestone country of England and Wales. But while the Peak, Mendip and Wales do have their own special attractions, it was significant that over half the sites in that guide were in the Yorkshire Dales. There are more caves in the Dales than in the rest of the country put together, and the same area is blessed with the finest of Britain's limestone landscapes. Without doubt, the Yorkshire Dales are limestone country at its best.

Limestone Caves

To appreciate limestone scenery, it is best to understand a little of both the processes and time scale behind its development. Limestone consists of the mineral calcite which chemically is calcium carbonate. The Carboniferous limestones were formed about 300 million years ago, and many millions of years later were folded, fractured, faulted and maybe mineralised while buried many kilometres beneath the surface. Then, within the last few million years, erosion has exposed the limestone at the surface, by removing the overlying rocks. Caves form in limestone because it is the one common rock dissolved by rainwater. The critical factor behind its solution is the amount of carbon dioxide there is in the water – more of it and more limestone can be dissolved; and rainwater gets its share of carbon dioxide merely from the atmosphere.

When rainwater lands on the limestone, it flows into the already existing fractures, and solution then slowly but steadily enlarges these into open fissures and even larger caves. The water flow through limestone may be fairly diffuse, or in a maze of fractures, or along major conduits; and it may be in the vadose zone above the water table or in the flooded, phreatic zone below. Caves can then form in all these patterns and environments. The highest of all carbon dioxide contents is found in soil water. So this water, seeping through into the rock, then dissolves the highest proportion of calcium carbonate. But when this lime-saturated water drips through into a cave, it loses carbon dioxide in order to reach equilibrium with the cave air; and consequently it has to precipitate calcite, again to maintain equilibrium. This is the origin of the stalactites and stalagmites in so many caves.

The different carbon dioxide contents of the soils, atmosphere and natural waters account for much of the processes and results of limestone solution and calcite deposition, particularly when the origin of the carbon dioxide is related to plant activity and in turn therefore to climate. This explains high solution rates and large caves in warmer climates (such as the tropics) and hardly any solution in glaciated landscapes devoid of vegetation. Similarly larger calcite deposits are found in warmer climates, and the contrast can even be seen between the caves of northern and southern England. So many details of cave erosion patterns and stalagmite shapes can be explained by consideration of the diffusion rates and changes in the water's carbon dioxide content. Just thinking in terms of carbon dioxide movement makes understanding cave processes so much easier.

Limestone Karst

Because limestone contains caves, its drainage is underground, and that is the identifying feature of a karst landscape (the word comes from an area of limestone in Yugoslavia). The diagnostic features of

Upper Long Churn Cave

karst are the dry hollows which would be lakes if it were not for their underground drainage; they may be known as closed depressions, blind valleys, shakeholes, sinkholes or dolines depending on their size and shape (they are described and explained as they are met on the walks in this guide). Other distinctive features of limestone karst are dry valleys, dry or active gorges, bare rock crags, limestone pavements, and of course the sinks and springs associated with the caves.

   More than any other landscape, karst is extraordinarily sensitive to climates both past and present. Particularly significant is whether or not there has been a past history of glaciation, and this is the main factor behind the overall differences in landscape character of the individual limestone areas of Britain. Nearly all the landscape

Ingleborough, seen across Chapel le Dale

Gordale

development has taken place in the last few million years, mostly in the period known to geologists as the Pleistocene. This was the time of periodic worldwide coolings which can be known as the Ice Age, when glaciers covered Britain as far south as London. Britain's recent history has not been simple, so its terminology can become rather complicated, but it is worth remembering that the 'Ice Age' can refer to either the whole long period of repeated glaciations, or to just one glaciation. Thinking of the glacial and climatic history is important in understanding the landscapes of Britain's limestone.

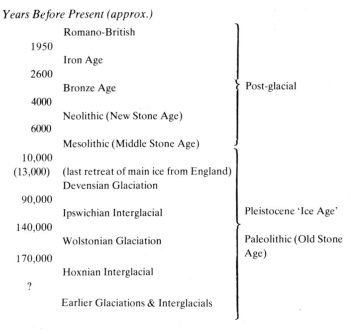

Years Before Present (approx.)

	Romano-British	
1950		
	Iron Age	
2600		
	Bronze Age	Post-glacial
4000		
	Neolithic (New Stone Age)	
6000		
	Mesolithic (Middle Stone Age)	
10,000		
(13,000)	(last retreat of main ice from England)	
	Devensian Glaciation	
90,000		
	Ipswichian Interglacial	Pleistocene 'Ice Age'
140,000		
	Wolstonian Glaciation	Paleolithic (Old Stone Age)
170,000		
	Hoxnian Interglacial	
?		
	Earlier Glaciations & Interglacials	

A simplified time scale – both geological and cultural

Limestone of the Yorkshire Dales

Across the southern part of the Yorkshire Dales National Park,
the Great Scar Limestone occupies the core of a block of country
known as the Craven Uplands, extending almost from Kirkby
Lonsdale to Pateley Bridge. Northwards the limestone dips gently
beneath the Yoredale rocks, which are mainly shale and sandstone
but do contain some more thin bands of limestone. To the south
the great geological fracture system known as the Craven Faults
separates the limestone Uplands from the Lowlands. And cutting
through the Craven Uplands, from north to south, and also out
to the east, are the glaciated valleys which are the Dales themselves.

Blocks of upland are formed by the limestone left standing
between the Dales. Their slopes are rimmed with long terraces of
white rock scars, and the plateau surfaces include great expanses
of limestone pavement. The high proportion of bare rock is
evidence of the region's recent deglaciation. Ice Age glaciers
covered the area only about 15,000 years ago, so, unlike the
limestone regions further south, the Yorkshire Dales have the
spectacular rock landscapes of a freshly glaciated karst. High
summit masses of shales and sandstone, notably forming the Three
Peaks, provide streams which flow on to the limestone and sink
into hundreds of caves.

The combination of spectacular landscapes and so many caves
makes the Yorkshire Dales a paradise for walkers, geologists,
geographers and outdoor people in general. The scenery of
Ingleborough, Malham and Wharfedale is textbook material with
a worldwide reputation, but throughout the area there are many
hidden gorges and secret caves which add character to a magnificent
stretch of countryside.

A Note on Footpaths

Every care has been taken in preparing this guide to include routes
which do not have access restrictions, but conditions can change

Ease Gill

and inclusion of a path does not form evidence of a right of way. Where permission is known to be needed it is mentioned. Most of the Dales limestone walks are on high country where there are minimal access problems. Perhaps the most crucial factor is the characteristic dry-stone walls; these should never be climbed, as they are easily damaged and are very difficult to repair – always find a gate or stile. Respect the walls, close the gates, keep dogs away from sheep and avoid litter – then walkers can continue their leisure in harmony with the farmers who work the land even in the National Park. The theme of the guide is limestone scenery, so the walks have been chosen to cover the best features. Many walks are therefore quite short, and it is left to the long-distance

enthusiasts to connect the walks for themselves into longer routes, using the many footpaths marked on OS maps. To aid location-finding, each site is given a national grid reference; for most sites it refers to the starting point of a walk, on a road, but for cave sites where the walk is not described it refers to the entrance.

Key to symbols used on maps

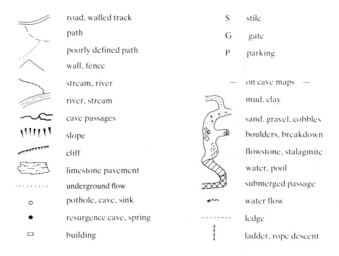

road, walled track	S	stile
path	G	gate
poorly defined path	P	parking
wall, fence		
stream, river	— on cave maps —	
river, stream	mud, clay	
cave passages	sand, gravel, cobbles	
slope	boulders, breakdown	
cliff	flowstone, stalagmite	
limestone pavement	water, pool	
underground flow	submerged passage	
pothole, cave, sink	water flow	
resurgence cave, spring	ledge	
building	ladder, rope descent	

Hunt Pot

A Note on Cave Exploration

Serious cave exploration is not within the scope of this guide.
Anyone wishing to pursue the armchair caving descriptions will
have to be, or become, a competent caver, normally as a member of
a club. All these caves require proper equipment – ropes, ladders,
helmets, strong lamps, warm clothing, good boots – and adequate
climbing ability, experience and preparation for getting very wet
and cold.

   To visit a cave with just a torch is not the conventional approach
to underground exploration, but it is reasonable in just a few cases.
These are in this book; but do not take this as a prompt to venture
further without proper guidance. The combination of darkness,

Ingleborough and its pavements

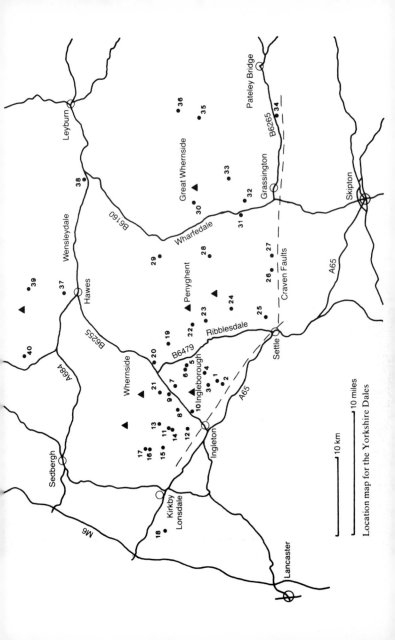

Location map for the Yorkshire Dales

water, and holes in the floor makes most caves simply dangerous to the inexperienced. The sport of caving has a notorious reputation – unfairly earned by the 95 per cent of accidents which happen to beginners due to sheer incompetence. Remember this when you first venture underground, and tackle only what is appropriate.

Good torches are vital to safety. Feeble pocket torches, half-dead batteries, or two people sharing a torch are recipes for disaster. Each person must have a good strong torch at least as powerful as a cycle lamp. Good lights are really worth while – they make for an enjoyable experience, instead of a dangerous stumble in the half-dark. Then have strong shoes, wellingtons or boots with good rubber soles; and a woolly hat is often a good idea.

Never go underground alone; avoid wet weather and the unpredictable threat of flooding; ensure the lights are good; and stick to the caves and passages in this guide. Follow these rules strictly, and a little cave exploration can be safe as well as enjoyable, interesting and exciting.

Yorkshire Dales: the walks

1 – Trow Gill

Of all the walks up on to the higher slopes of Ingleborough, that
from Clapham is justifiably the most popular. It takes in an unusual
nature reserve, the Ingleborough Show Cave, the spectacular gorge
of Trow Gill and the famous pothole of Gaping Gill. It is Britain's
finest introduction to limestone scenery.

Since the by-pass took the traffic away, Clapham village has
regained some of its atmosphere of rural charm. The peace is
slightly frayed at summer weekends when it receives so many
visitors, but it has never matched the tourist crowding of Malham;
there is a large car park with a National Park visitor centre at the
lower end of the village. From there it is a pleasant walk up beside
the beck past the variety of cottages and the fine church of St James
with its fourteenth-century tower (though the rest was rebuilt in
1814). Keep left of the beck and round the corner to the sawmill
which is the entrance to the grounds of the Ingleborough Estate.
The path behind climbs a steep slope so thickly vegetated that it is
hardly recognisable as an earth dam. From its crest, the lake extends
into Clapdale.

Through the last century the Farrer family lived at Ingleborough
Hall, and they planned and worked their estate with commendable
boldness. They planted the woods, dammed the lake, opened the
cave, and rebuilt the village. It is to their credit that they created
such a fine landscape. The walk beside the lake and on up into the
woods is always a delight. For botanists it is much more than that.
Between 1900 and 1920, Reginald Farrer travelled the east and
brought back many specimens to plant in his woodland; even the
inexpert will recognise the clumps of Himalayan bamboo as a
species alien to the Yorkshire Dales. Limestone is the bedrock
through most of the woods, but rhododendrons dislike a lime soil,
and an area rich in them, close to the end of the lake, marks the
outcrop of some slates. These rocks underlie the limestone, but the
North Craven Fault is a great step in the geological structure and

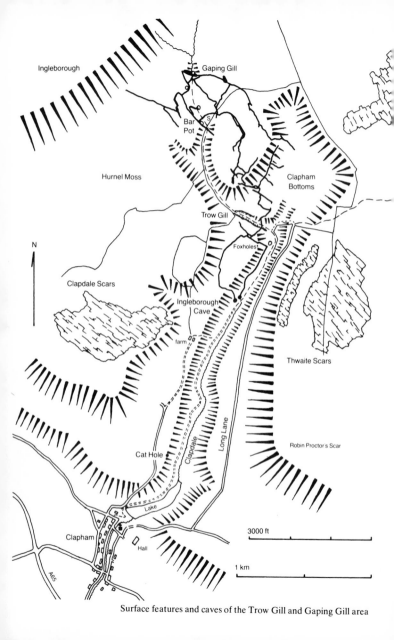

Surface features and caves of the Trow Gill and Gaping Gill area

erosion across it has exposed just a slice of the older rocks in the floor of Clapdale. The cleaved slates can be seen in the streambed which descends from Cat Hole, a resurgence from the limestone only active in wet weather.

Just beyond the Cat Hole streambed, the dale is again cut all in limestone, and the path winds through the woods with occasional views down to the beck flowing through a rocky gorge. The Grotto is an over-ornamental shelter built beside the path; just why the Victorian walkers chose to rest in its dark confines remains a mystery. Clapdale opens out a little and the woods come to an end; the valley is a bowl of short green turf broken by the odd scar of white bedrock – so typical of limestone country. Beside the beck, a low blockhouse emits an eerie clanking for it houses a ram pump driving water to Clapdale Farm not far above in the woods. The beck is of course an anomaly in a limestone valley, but hopes of following it far are short-lived. Just beside a stone bridge, the water emerges from the rock mouth of Clapham Beck Head, meeting daylight for the first time since it plunged into the sinkholes high on the limestone plateau. Almost above the resurgence lies the entrance to Ingleborough Cave, a show cave well worth visiting (see page 35) for its underground scenery which is the natural complement to Clapdale and Trow Gill.

Above the resurgence Clapdale is normally dry – a sheltered glen with a grassy floor between low scars of limestone. A low cave entrance on the left has a short crawl into the noisy wet passages of Beck Head Stream Cave, another part of the underground drainage from Gaping Gill. Totally different in character is Foxholes, a dry rock shelter in a side valley just above the track; there is little to see there now, but Neolithic pottery fragments and bone implements unearthed within it show that it was used as a shelter some 4000 years ago. The main valley sweeps round to the left and a gateway takes the path straight towards the rocky confines of Trow Gill.

Rising steadily, the valley floor is overlooked by slopes which become higher and steeper. At first, the right bank is a grass slope on glacial boulder clay, while the left wall is terraced limestone crags. Then the gorge narrows between vertical rock more than 25 m high on each side. On the left a major bedrock joint keeps the cliff arrow-straight, but the right wall closes till the ravine is only a couple of metres wide. A run of boulders provides a steep scramble up through the narrows, until the rock gorge abruptly ends where it opens out into a grassy dry valley. Trow Gill is a classic example of a limestone gorge. It is often thought of as a collapsed cavern, but there is no evidence that a roof once existed. In fact, it was cut by a surface stream of meltwater flowing off the limestone plateau as the glaciers died away at the end of the last Ice Age; at that time ground freezing ensured that the existing caves were sealed by ice. Where the stream flowed over some strong beds of limestone, to drop into Clapdale, it developed a waterfall in the retreat gorge which rapidly cut into the hill. Water-scoured hollows can be seen in the walls of the narrow section, and the bedding plane cave just below is merely a wall notch of no great extent. When the Ice Age climate ameliorated, the drainage went back underground, and the gorge has survived because there is no surface water to degrade its walls.

The short-lived meltwater torrent, which once cascaded down Trow Gill, also formed the valley cut into the limestone plateau above. Now dry, the valley provides shelter for the path as it meanders gently and rises slowly, but its upper end just fades away. A stile takes the path over a wall, to continue up a last low crag on to the wide open spaces of Ingleborough's broad limestone bench. Immediately on the left a rocky pothole is the first of many entrances to the great cave system of Gaping Gill whose network of passages underlies all this part of the fell. Bar Pot is the name of this one and it is the easiest way into the system for cavers; 10 m below moor level the boulder floor of the open pothole reveals the entrance under one wall, but don't venture in as there is a deep shaft just inside.

Beyond Bar Pot there are great banks of bog-covered boulder clay, but the path continues on the drier turf of the limestone soil. Flood Entrance Pot lies just to the right of the path. It is an inconspicuous little hole, but in 1909 it became the first dry route into the Gaping Gill cave system. Still a popular sporting cave, it has a series of narrow rifts and descents leading to the lip of a most impressive 40 m deep shaft, at the foot of which lies one of the main tunnels of the low-level system. Back on the surface, there is rather too much glacial sediment and peat bog overlying the limestone, and the way is sometimes wet underfoot. Many shakeholes pit the moor where sediment has been washed down into the limestone; open caves lie at the foot of some, and in a few cases provide yet more entrances to the complex of caves below.

Poorly defined paths straggle across the fell. Those towards the right aim for the obvious fenced depression around Gaping Gill; this magnificent pothole warrants further attention (see page 39). Curving up the slope to the left, paths rise from the limestone bench and head for the summit of Ingleborough; this can be a good way to extend the walk into a day's outing for there are fine views from the summit ridge. But beware the onset of cloud or mist because it can be quite difficult to find the correct route down off the plateau.

On the return journey, a worthwhile variation is to take the high-level route alongside Clapdale. From the gate at the foot of Trow Gill, turn north on a path into a shallow ravine. This was another meltwater channel, in this case just cut through the terminal moraine left by the glacier as a barrier across the head of Clapdale. The path leads out into Clapham Bottoms – a broad dry bowl of pasture with just a few crags of limestone breaking through the veneer of glacial sediment. As the slope on the right eases, cut up to a track which aims back through a gateway in the dry-stone wall. This leads on to Long Lane, an old bridleway connecting Clapham and Selside in Ribblesdale. A short way down the lane there is an excellent view across to Trow Gill, its bare limestone walls contrasting with the grass slopes of the Clapdale moraine just to its right.

The walk down Long Lane provides open views across the top of Clapdale, which shelters in the woods below. Limestone crags of Clapdale and Thwaite Scars fringe the dale on each side. The lane dips down where it crosses the line of the North Craven Fault. Off to the left, the limestone on the north side of the fault ends in the prow of Robin Proctor's Scar, while south of the fault the limestone was displaced to a much lower level in earth movements millions of years ago. Thwaite Lane is met at a T-junction; this was the ancient highway along the south side of Ingleborough, predating the turnpike which is at a lower level. Turn right and follow it down

through the grounds of Ingleborough Hall – and through the two
tunnels built by the Farrers to protect the privacy of the Hall
grounds. The tunnelled lane ends by the church at the top end of
Clapham village and the car park is not far down to the left.

The southern flank of Ingleborough contains some of Britain's
finest limestone scenery. It is the textbook area where schools come
to study karst, and it also provides excellent walking; Clapdale,
Trow Gill and Gaping Gill should not be missed by anyone who
wants to see what the Pennine landscapes have to offer.

All the walk is on public footpaths, except for the stretch through
the woods of the Ingleborough Estate, and this is open all through
the year on payment of a small fee.

2 – Ingleborough Cave   754711

A rock amphitheatre, above and left of Clapham Beck Head,
contains a broad low arch which is the entrance to Ingleborough
Cave. In the early years of the last century, the underground
caverns between the famous Gaping Gill Hole and Clapham Beck
Head were totally unknown and remained a source of mystery and
wonder. Gaping Gill was an unapproachable abyss of fearsome
depth, and the Beck Head had a rock roof meeting black water only
just out of daylight. Ingleborough Cave was then only a short
gallery, blocked a few metres in by a wall of stalagmite beyond
which only a tiny airspace over deep water stretched into the
darkness.

Occasional outbursts of flood water did suggest that this short
cave might be connected to the underground river of Gaping Gill.
So in 1837 the landowner ordered the stalagmite barrier to be
broken down, to drain away the lake and allow access to the
interior. The operation was a success and the workmen walked into
a fine cavern which reached a quarter of the way to Gaping Gill.
However it took another 146 years of spasmodic exploration
before the final link in the underground route was found in 1983.

Most of the passage explored in 1837 is now open as a show cave,

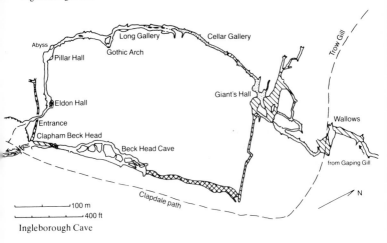

Ingleborough Cave

and a visit is well worth the walk up Clapdale from the road at
Clapham village. The entrance leads straight into a gallery nearly 3
m high and wide, with stalagmite banks lining each wall. The roof is
an almost level bedding plane with lines of tiny stalactites picking
out the joint lines. After 20 m the route narrows through the
stalagmite banks reached in 1837, but widens immediately beyond.
The old water level, so close to the roof, is marked by clear lines on
the stalagmite walls. A group of stalactites which used to hang down
into the lake have been encrusted with a globular form of calcite
where they were submerged, and are now descriptively known as
the Inverted Forest. The lower roof just beyond is a uniform
bedding plane, but many a visitor has commented that it looks more
like a deck of concrete beams; the appearance is created by a
remarkably consistent set of joints which have been picked out by
solution in the roof bed of limestone.

The roof steps up into Eldon Hall where calcite deposits still
mark the old lake levels. A fine bank of calcite flowstone, known as
the Mushroom Bed, was built out by a tiny inlet of saturated water
but truncated at its base where calcite could not be deposited
beneath the old lake surface. At the end of the Hall, the path rises

past another calcite barrier broken down in 1837; a higher pool
level is marked on the walls and it is easy to see why the calcite dam
is referred to as a rimstone deposit. Most of the stalactite deposits in
this part of the cave are dead, due to drainage changes in the rock
above, but patches of white show where deposition continues. The
passage continues as a fine broad canyon with plentiful stalagmite
till it rises out of the old lake into the much wider Pillar Hall.

Pools in the hall are crystal clear and are floored by the globular
encrusting calcite deposits which characteristically form
underwater; they are best described by the American term, cave
popcorn. Beyond the stalagmite pillar which has joined to the
ceiling and given a name to the chamber, the Abyss is a rather
grandly named rift which swallows a small stream from further in
the cave. Upstream the cave continues past some fine calcite
curtains and then widens to a splendid section with a broad oxbow
passage on the left. The path has been entrenched through a layer of
cobbles and into bedrock, but still the roof comes lower. First the
visitor has to stoop a little, and then crouch down for a few metres
of energetic 'gorilla walk'.

Blissful relief appears at a high cross rift known as the Gothic
Arch. This is the largest of a number of sites in the cave where
solution has etched out joints above the level of the bedding planes
which control most of the passage roof. The upward solution proves
that the cave was full of water when it was formed. Indeed, the cave
is very old, probably over a quarter of a million years. It was once
the main drainage route from Gaping Gill and contained water
under pressure because it predates Clapdale. Much later Clapdale
was cut, so that the cave became free-draining, and then the
underground river, only able to erode the floor, cut the broad
canyon which sweeps upstream of the Gothic Arch. Later still, the
cave river found a new lower route through Beck Head Cave, and
Ingleborough Cave was abandoned high and dry except for
occasional flood pulses and the continuous drip of the seepage
water which has built up the calcite deposits.

The last section of the show cave is the finely sculptured canyon
of the Long Gallery. It too once contained a lake, but the calcite
'tide-line' shows it was only ankle-deep. The passage widens until it

Flowstone in Ingleborough Cave

is a flattened T-shape; the wide slot first formed on the bedding
plane has the later canyon only incised across part of its width.
Upstream, the canyon slowly loses its depth until the end of the path
is reached at a shallow pool. Across the pool, a bank of sediment
can just be seen completely blocking the canyon's continuation –
the consequence of inwash by meltwater at the end of the last Ice
Age. On the shelf on the right, the Pool of Reflections doubles the
image of a group of stalactites. Much wider is the shelf to the left,
and deep in its shadows a low passage continues to the inner parts of
the cave.

Only accessible for cavers, the way on starts as the sandy Cellar Gallery, but then joins the main underground stream, and becomes a low and very wet series of passages which pass right beneath the Trow Gill gorge. Eventually only divers can continue, through permanently flooded tunnels, until they can climb up into the fossil passages which are part of the Gaping Gill system. The route through is long and complex, and it is fortunate indeed that the best of the passages are so accessible at the bottom end. Ingleborough Cave provides a spectacular and memorable insight into the most famous piece of underground Britain.

The show cave is open daily from April to October and also at weekends through the winter.

3 – Gaping Gill   751727

It takes its name from the gaping pothole which engulfs Fell Beck high on the slopes of Ingleborough. It is probably the best-known pothole in the country. It is in the record books for having the highest waterfall, the deepest shaft and the largest cave chamber in Britain. Even though it is so conspicuously atypical, it is the pothole most commonly referred to in geography textbooks. And because it is so atypical, and spectacular, Gaping Gill is well worth the effort of a special visit.

Gaping Gill is best reached by the walk up through Clapdale and Trow Gill, though the road is slightly nearer in Crummack Dale. The wide bowl of Clapham Bents is catchment for the largest stream on the upper slopes of Ingleborough. Fell Beck collects many tributaries before it levels its course across the blanket of boulder clay on the limestone plateau. The beck has cut down into the boulder clay, forming a valley some 10 m deep, until it is deep enough to have found the underlying limestone. After a few metres flowing over the bare rock, Fell Beck reaches the open pothole and plunges underground. The boulder clay valley is blind, and most visitors approach Gaping Gill over its end rim to see Fell Beck disappear into blackness almost beneath their feet.

The wide open hole, of obviously great depth, was a blatant

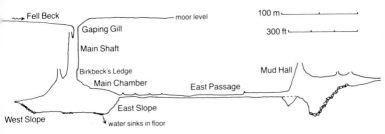

Cross section through Gaping Gill

challenge to the adventurers of the last century, but the cascading water was not to be easily defeated even when most of it was diverted into other sinkholes. In 1842 a local man, John Birkbeck, reached a ledge 60 m down but was awed to see the shaft still dropping out of sight. Later that century the first caving clubs started their explorations in the area, but it was much to the chagrin of the Yorkshiremen that Gaping Gill was first descended by a Frenchman! The widely-travelled caver Edouard Martel reached the floor of the shaft more than 100 m down in August 1895. Since then, many cavers have descended the great pothole; and down below they have discovered more than 15 km of passages which lace their way through the limestone between Gaping Gill and Ingleborough Cave. The discoveries have included other, much easier, entrances; Bar Pot and others like it are now the normally used routes into the main underground system.

A descent of the shaft is today therefore a bit of a rarity. It normally requires a good spell of dry weather, a very long rope, and a lot of effort and experience. But for two weeks each summer, two of the major local caving clubs rig a winch at Gaping Gill, so that visitors may descend in the relative comfort of a bosun's chair. To the clubs it is a fund-raising exercise, but for the non-caving visitor it is a golden opportunity to see a very spectacular cave.

To give an almost dry descent, Fell Beck is diverted into fissures in its bed just upstream of the shaft. A gantry is rigged across a corner of the hole so that the bosun's chair has a clear descent, and the winch is bolted to the rock platform just beside it. From the gantry there is a splendid view downwards, seemingly to oblivion; Gaping Gill Hole is 5–10 m in diameter with vertical or overhanging walls. (Without the gantry in place it is very difficult to see down, and it is horrifying to see how close some tourists step to the edge.) Once the intrepid visitor is in the winch seat, the safety plank is slid out from below him – revealing just blackness. For a few metres the descent is slow, close to the wall; then the chair hangs clear. From that point on the descent is an experience akin to that gained on the very worst of funfair rides. The bosun's chair drops under gravity; a guide cable keeps it on the right line; with eyes unadjusted to the gloom, almost nothing is seen – except the circle of daylight above, receding and shrinking; a long, long, long way down, the winch brakes are applied; the floor emerges from the shadows, and the visitor steps out of the chair. He is then standing in the middle of a vast chamber, and slowly his eyes adjust to take in the scene.

The Main Chamber of Gaping Gill is the largest cavern in Britain; it is 140 m long and around 30 m high and wide. The floor is almost level sand and gravel, with boulder slopes at each end. The roof rises towards the centre where it is broken by the Main Shaft and some other parallel shafts. Daylight streams in, and just about reaches every corner of the chamber. Normally Fell Beck crashes down with the daylight, but when the winch is on it is diverted and pours down the subsidiary shafts to the left. It adds up to a magnificent sight in either case. The shafts enter close to the north wall where vertical rock is washed clean by the spray of floodwater. Most of the chamber roof is then a great sloping overhang, falling from the shafts to the south. This is the clue to the origin of such a large chamber. Two sets of fracture break the limestone; vertical joints control the line of the main shaft, and an inclined fault forms the chamber roof. The intersection of the fractures provided optimum conditions for efficient erosion when found by the waters of Fell Beck.

From both ends of the chamber, passages head off into the rambling complex of low-level caves. Unfortunately the best of the passages are at the remoter ends of the system, so can only be visited by fully equipped cavers, and the Fell Beck water cannot be followed out of the chamber as it sinks into the boulders and gravel

The main chamber of Gaping Gill

of its floor. East Passage is a very ancient dry tunnel at the top of the
east boulder slope and it can be followed to the large but extremely
gloomy Mud Hall. South Passage is another abandoned tunnel
which leads either to the spacious Sand Cavern, or through to the
foot of the shafts from Bar Pot and Flood Entrance Pot. Both
passages require only a helmet and lamp, but they contain hidden
junctions and deep holes in their floors which mean that it is only
safe to visit them when accompanied by an experienced caver;
neither really lives up to the splendour of the Main Chamber.

The highlight of any visit to Gaping Gill is however the ascent
back up the shaft. It takes nearly five minutes to be slowly hauled up
by the winch, and this gives a marvellous opportunity to appreciate
the dimensions of the cave. The bosun's chair leaves the flat floor of
the chamber and rises vertically into space. The walls are way out of
reach, and people left on the floor shrink into the distance. Nearly
two minutes later and 40 m up, the suspended visitor is still in the
chamber, and he has an awe-inspiring bat's-eye view of it. At 45 m
he enters the shaft, at this depth more than 15 m across; Birkbeck's
famous ledge breaks one wall, dark alcoves spout water from the
other walls. The silent ascent continues – there are still 60 m to go.
In wet weather, sprays of water emerge from fissures beneath
overhangs; but slowly the walls close in, the light gets brighter, and
the silhouette of the winch gantry turns into a solid platform
surrounded by the grassy slopes of the open fell.

There is nothing else in Britain remotely like the winch descent of
Gaping Gill. The shaft, the waterfalls and the chamber are in a
totally different league from any other British cave. An opportunity
to visit Gaping Gill should not be missed – it is a memorable
experience.

The winch is on Gaping Gill for just two periods of ten days each,
ending with the Spring and Late Summer Bank Holiday Mondays.
There are restrictions on young children, and it is best to avoid late
afternoons at the weekends when prohibitively long queues may
build up for the return ascent.

4 – Juniper Gulf

Even the name of Juniper Gulf is rather splendid. The word 'Gulf' evokes images of bottomless chasms and dark mysteries. And fortunately it does live up to its name. Underground it provides one of Britain's great experiences in vertical caving, and up in the daylight world this is matched by a remote location in the heart of the Ingleborough limestone country.

Juniper can be approached from any of three directions, but the best way is from Crummack Dale in the east. There is a narrow road up from Austwick, one of the most charming of the villages around Ingleborough, and it climbs the hill past Norber where the famous glacial erratics lie on the scar up the footpath to the west. The road runs out of tarmac but it's a good gravel track which continues to Crummack Farm where cars can be parked. Through a gate on the left, a path leads up a shallow valley which cuts through the scars formed by the lowest beds of limestone.

In a very short distance the valley dies out, and ahead lie the wide open spaces of Long Scar and the Allotment. This great, almost level, limestone bench extends far to both right and left. It was scoured by ice moving from the north during the last Ice Age, ice which spread out from the edge of the great Ribblesdale glacier, crossed the limestone plateau, and some of which carved out the headless valley of Crummack Dale. Thin boulder clay and soils now support dry springy grass across much of the area, but there is a large slab of rather broken limestone pavements forming the upper end of Long Scar. Far ahead the slopes rise to the summit mass of Ingleborough, and this is the best guide for the walker, as there is a maze of paths and tracks; just aim north-west for the skyline summit. This tends to follow an easy line with a path following the bedrock joints through the main belts of limestone pavements. Near the end of the pavements there is a substantial dry-stone wall, and a gate involves a minimal diversion to the left. Through the gate, turn well to the right across fairly featureless grassland, and Juniper Gulf is just over half a kilometre away in the second shallow valley coming down from Ingleborough.

The entrance of Juniper Gulf is quite distinctive, though it cannot

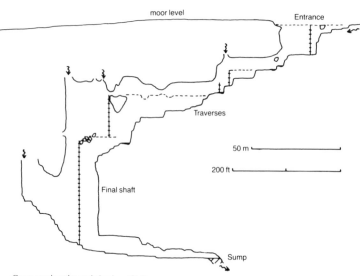

Cross section through Juniper Gulf

be seen from afar. Grass pasture extends right to the lip, and a rift 30 m long and less than 5 m wide cuts into the rock. A gravel floor lies 20 m below, and a stream cascades down a narrow slot from the moor at the Ingleborough end. The water flows across the floor and tumbles over boulders into a dark rift at the other end. The rim of this tantalising rift, with the water dropping into blackness, is journey's end for all but the fully equipped caver. But for those who can continue, the descent of Juniper Gulf is one of Britain's classic underground experiences.

Both the long entrance rift and the entire cave passage lie in a straight line, for the cave is developed on a small fault which cuts cleanly through the limestone. Many thousands of years ago the stream first found its way along the fault, and ever since then it has just cut downwards, following the same line. The result is a sequence of long narrow fissures connected by wider shafts where waterfalls have more easily cut into the smooth rock walls. From the

The final shaft of Juniper Gulf

floor of the entrance rift an easy climb down over the boulders leads to a short passage and a pair of cascades where ladders are again needed. Beyond these the rift passage continues, arrow-straight, but the stream drops into a narrow slot, and the exciting caving starts.

As the floor slot is too narrow to pass in places, the caver has to continue by traversing along ledges in the upper part of the ever-deepening fissure. A thin shale bed within the limestone has been eaten out by the water of bygone years, so a convenient pair of ledges breaks the smooth vertical walls of the fissure. They make for fairly easy traversing, even if the aspect is a little airy where the fissure widens out below, and there are a few places where the ledges are less than adequate and demand some delicate acrobatics from the visitor. In such style the route continues, until the ledges abruptly end and the walls bell out into a smooth shaft. It is 25 m to the floor and straight into another ledge traverse. But this quickly leads to a tangle of boulders jammed in the rift, making a floor to a small chamber. The stream is far below, heard but not seen, and the walls rise sheer into the blackness above. At the far side of the little chamber is a big black void – the impressive final shaft of Juniper Gulf.

Starting down the ladder from that little chamber is the climax of the descent of Juniper. The floor of jammed boulders is only a few metres thick, so almost immediately the ladder, and the caver, is in the middle of space. The shaft is beautiful, with the ladder hanging plum down its centre for more than 60 m. The walls are fluted by the action of dripping water, and are horizontally banded by the contrasting layers in the limestone. In plan the shaft is a long slot and at one end the stream hisses down, making a distant roar where it hits the rock floor. This vertical panorama is slowly unfolded by the headlight of the caver as he plods down the ladder. The rock floor comes to meet him, and the lower rift passage beckons to the way on. A series of cascades leads down between water-polished walls of cream-coloured limestone, and the rift abruptly ends where the stream slides into a deep and dark sump pool, just 130 m below the grass covered moors. Juniper Gulf is vertical caving at its best.

Permission to descend Juniper Gulf is obtained from the Ingleborough Estates Office.

5 – Alum Pot   775756

The most spectacular entrance shaft, or pothole, in Britain is Alum
Pot. Not as deep as Gaping Gill, nor as wide as Hull Pot, it
combines depth, width and spectacular viewpoints in a unique style.
The origin of its name is obscure, but it may be a distortion of Helln
Pot, and if that conjures up visions of a descent into the underworld
then it is not out of place.

Alum Pot lies on the eastern slopes of Ingleborough, just above
the little hamlet of Selside. Even though it dates back to a mention
in the Domesday Book, Selside has never grown beyond a few
farms; it once had an annual cheese fair of some note, but that died
out late in the last century. Just out of the north end of the village,
the main road takes a bend, and a rocky track leaves towards the
west. Cars can be driven some way up it and there is room to leave
them on the verges; rarely are there only a few cars here at a
weekend. Continue up the walled track to the corner where it turns
left and heads over the limestone plateau as the old packhorse route
to Clapham. From the corner, a single clump of trees can be seen
higher on the fell; they mark the position of Alum Pot. Over a stile,
an unfenced track winds up grassy slopes, diminishes to a footpath
and continues into a shallow dry valley above some low limestone
scars and a few springs. It leads right to the dry-stone wall which
surrounds the pothole.

The safest viewpoint is from the path round to the left, in line
with the long axis of the surface opening. The open hole is nearly 40
m long and over 10 m wide; at the far end it is 65 m deep. Alum Pot
has formed on a single massive fracture which cuts vertically
through the limestone. A small beck falls into its southern end,
dropping vertically as a mist of heavy rain; in dry weather its flow
ceases, but in a very hard winter it creates a magnificent sight by
draping the full depth of the pot in a sheet of sparkling ice. The beck
was once much larger, as most of its flow has now been deflected
through the Long Churn caves. Alum Pot's large size is also due to
the other passage which enters its northern end – it can be seen in
the shadows some 20 m down and was once another stream route
from the caves up the fell.

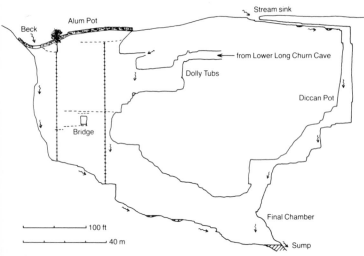

Cross section through Alum and Diccan Pots

Extreme care is essential from anyone going inside the wall,
though to do so is worth while for a much better view down the
shaft. The larches and pines, planted in 1874, thrived inside the wall
away from the hunger that sheep have for young shoots, and one of
them now provides a natural balustrade on the viewpoint. Over the
stile, take the very narrow path for the few metres to the second tree
which grows right on the lip of the shaft (though it is not in good
health, and either it or the rock will one day become unsafe). From
the tree, the view down is spectacular. The floor is just 50 m below,
ribbed limestone sprayed by the falling beck. Halfway down, broad
ledges can be seen on both sides of the shaft, linked by the Bridge –
an enormous slab of rock which has peeled off the wall and leans
across the shaft with its base on the lower ledge. Over to the right
the dark opening is the cavers' route in; from it they ladder down on
to the upper ledge, walk round the far side, cross the Bridge to the
nearside lower ledge and follow that to a last 15 m drop directly
below the tree.

Alum Pot

Alum Pot was first descended in 1847 by a team who came in by
the now-popular route through Lower Long Churn Cave, but they
were stopped by another waterfall just below the daylight shaft.
They returned the next year and made a direct descent of the shaft,
then continuing down the waterfall and into the massive rift passage
which leads to the final chamber. There, a powerful cascade pours
from the roof, and all the water disappears into a deep sump pool;
this is at the same level as the resurgence at Turn Dub, over 2 km
away and on the far side of the River Ribble. The wet way in, via
Diccan Pot, was not completely explored until 1932, for it is a
dramatic piece of cave with two waterfalls of 40 m to be descended,
the last one into the Alum Pot chamber. To descend the waterfalls
of Diccan and then regain the surface by the long rope climb up
Alum Pot is, in cavers' terms, a very short trip, but its impressive
vertical scenery makes it one of the great experiences in Yorkshire
caving.

Before leaving Alum Pot, return outside the wall and take the
path round to another stile at the northern end. This leads over to
the grassy bank where there is another magnificent view along the
length of this giant open rift, which is particularly impressive when
the beck is cascading down the far end. There is no denying that
Alum Pot is a remarkable shaft, which must do more than fulfil
anyone's concept of a limestone pothole; and it is very much a part
of the Ingleborough landscape.

Alum Pot is on private land, and a small access fee is payable at
Selside Farm in the village.

6 – Long Churn Cave   774757

In complete contrast to the vertical shaft of Alum Pot, Long Churn
Cave is an almost horizontal system which has very easy access. It is
part of a whole complex of caves formed in a series of bedding
planes close to the top of the limestone. Streams from the upper
slopes of South House Moor and Borrins Moor, including the main
flow of Alum Pot Beck, sink into the limestone but then flow

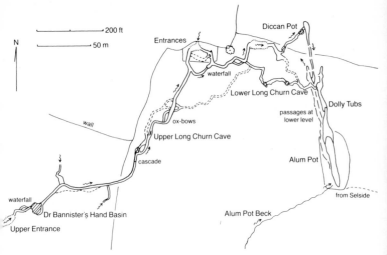

The Long Churn Caves and Alum Pot

through the 3 km of known caves only just below the surface. They follow down the very gentle dip of the limestones, towards the north-east, until they eventually plunge to depth on the major fracture which houses both Alum and Diccan Pots. Even though it is so close to the surface, the main passage in this sytem is one of the finest streamways in the Pennines.

From Alum Pot, continue along the path and then head across the fell towards the only visible tree. Over to the right a short section of stream is visible, emerging from one cave and dropping into another. It comes out of Long Churn Cave through a low wet passage which is fortunately not the only entrance. It flows into Diccan Pot; this passage too is rather low and contains some deep pools before ending at the lip of the first deep waterfall. Back above ground, a corner of the field left of the tree has been fenced off around the main Long Churn entrances. Beyond an open rift, there is another section of unroofed cave passage, with entrances at both

ends, but it has only a small stream coming from yet another cave beyond the wall.

Take the left entrance; it is stooping height with a shallow puddle in the middle of the floor. A good torch soon penetrates the darkness, as eyes adjust to the gloom, and the noise of water beckons from ahead. It is only a few metres to a junction, where the stream rushes from right to left in a clean-washed passage carved in cream-coloured limestone. This is the Upper Long Churn streamway, and upstream is a delight to explore. There is always a good stream in this passage, but – a word of warning: keep away in bad weather, because drainage ditches on the moor above mean that it responds very rapidly to flooding, and rainfall can quickly turn a playful stream into a dangerous torrent. In stable, dry weather, go ahead. Be prepared to get wet feet. It takes a lot of effort and some skill to do the passage dry. Wellingtons and a modicum of effort will suffice, and this adds a little to the challenge, as some of the pools are just over knee-deep. But wet feet are a small price to pay to see this splendid passage.

Upstream it starts as a canyon 2 m high and wide. The roof is a flat bedding plane, and the walls and floor are finely scalloped by eddies in the water. For part of the way, the shallow stream glides swiftly over polished rock, but further on there are banks of boulders and cobbles, and also deeper pools. At roof level the bedding plane widens out each side and there are a number of side loops and branches, though nearly all are low crawls. Then there is an oxbow on the right; a clean dry floor, in a passage now only active in flood conditions, avoids the first part of a longer pool. More boulders on the floor, a flake of bedrock with the stream flowing both sides of it, and then the roof lifts to nearly 4 m. There is a deeper pool, and the oxbow on the right is at a higher level – not worth the climb. Round a double bend and the next pool has a small cascade into its far side; the faint-hearted may turn back, but the pool is not too deep and the scramble out is easy – all part of the fun of caving.

A few more pools, and the passage reverts to a canyon a couple of

A cascade inside Long Churn Cave

metres high. It is a good metre wide at stream level, but the roof is much wider, with broad notches into the bedding plane on either side. Clearly the bedding plane was the initial weakness in the limestone; water found it and flowed sluggishly along, meandering around with many side loops. It opened up a low wide slot, and only later, when the opening was large enough to carry the flow with ease, did the stream start to move faster and carve a trench into the rock floor; then it did not need the width, and the one deep, narrow canyon developed while the rest of the bedding plane was left high and dry. Sediment has been left on some of the ledges, and since then percolation water has deposited stalactites on the ceiling – some old, corroded and bulbous, others smaller and fringing the joint lines.

Where the floor rises over a few rapids, and the roof stays level, the passage shrinks to stooping height, but the sound of falling water beckons from ahead. Suddenly the canyon widens into a low chamber, 10 m in diameter, with nearly the whole floor occupied by the pool known as Dr Bannister's Hand Basin. The entire stream cascades into the pool, coming down a steep chute which has cut back from a high roof fissure; it is a noisy and dramatic spot. For those who are tall, do not mind getting a little wet, have good boots, and have helmet lamps leaving both hands free, the 5 m climb up the cascade is easy; and the top is within sight of daylight from the upper entrance. But the Hand Basin is a good climax to a visit to Long Churn, and it is far more enjoyable and interesting to return down the cave.

Don't go downstream from the junction with the entrance passage, for it is low and leads shortly to a waterfall. Instead, emerge from the entrance and go straight into the second entrance just a few metres ahead. This leads underneath the open rift to daylight, and then back to the stream just below the waterfall, which is a fine sight. The stream has dropped to a new lower bedding plane, and follows this through Lower Long Churn Cave. There is a short walking section of passage then a couple of deep pools before the water escapes to daylight beneath a very low roof. A dry passage on the right is the cavers' route to Alum Pot. It is easy going at first but then there are two very deep pools requiring careful traverses, and a pair of climbs, so it is best left to cavers who are properly dressed and equipped. There is anyway a 15 m shaft needing a ladder to reach the final passages which ends on the ledge giving the marvellous view from halfway down the Alum Pot shaft.

Many people have had their first taste of caving at Alum Pot, for the whole system provides an excellent introduction to the sport. Proper equipment and experienced leaders are needed for many parts of the cave, but the 250 m of the Upper Long Churn streamway is easy enough to demand only a strong torch. Even if the sport is not the appeal, the cave is well worth a visit for its almost unrivalled insight into the underground drainage of limestone country.

The caves are on private land, and a small access fee is payable at Selside Farm in the village.

7 – Great Douk Cave   745777

Around the northern end of Ingleborough, the broad limestone bench provides spectacular and easy walking, and is easily reached from the Chapel le Dale road. Caves, sinkholes, scars and pavements are in abundance, and, perhaps more than anywhere else, a short walk can cover a textbook range of limestone landforms. Not only is it a grand introduction to karst scenery, but the Great Douk area offers some excellent views and there is also an accessible cave.

Just north of the Hill Inn, there is a lay-by on the left, and a footpath leaves the road signposted to Great Douk Cave. It is easy walking, following the contours on the rich turf of the limestone benches, and past an old lime kiln on the left. Ahead and to the left rise a few more low terraces in the upper beds of the limestone and then steep dark slopes climb to the Ingleborough ridge. After the stile there is an excellent view down Chapel le Dale, with its broad U-shape profile providing the classic evidence for its past glaciation. Beyond it, Twistleton Scars rise to Scales Moor where the sun may catch the white of the extensive pavements.

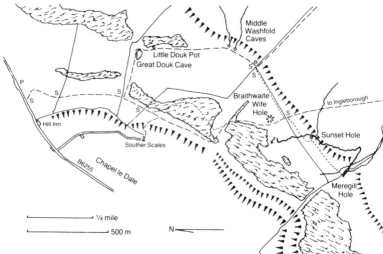

Middle
Washfold
Caves

Little Douk Pot
Great Douk Cave

Braithwaite
Wife
Hole

to Ingleborough

P

Hill Inn

Souther Scales

Sunset Hole

Chapel le Dale
B6255

Meregill
Hole

¼ mile

500 m

N

The area around Great Douk Cave

Over the third stile turn left up the shallow dry valley to Great
Douk Cave. The entrance is a collapse depression, about 50 m by
20 m with walls, mostly vertical, dropping 15 m to a breakdown
floor. It is ringed by a sheep fence but there is a way over just to the
right and a path down to the floor of the hole. At the far end, a
stream emerges from a large cave entrance, and then sinks into the
boulders. A 2 m waterfall must be climbed to get into the cave – it
requires a little care, is easier going up than down, and involves
getting wet when the stream is high. The cave can then safely be
explored for a little way with just the aid of a good torch. Ignore the
low inlet on the left, and take the main passage through a little
chamber. It continues to follow the stream in a pleasant clean
canyon 3 m high and wide. Meandering around, it narrows and goes
through another small chamber before broken rocks on the floor
mark the approach to Little Douk Pot. Daylight streams down the
vertical shaft from 15 m above. Deep water is a barrier to further
progress, so return the 100 m downstream to Great Douk, and
appreciate it as a fine piece of stream cave.

A path loops round the edge of the collapse hole, then heads south to pass Little Douk Pot – which looks far better from below. A low scar on the left marks the edge of a limestone pavement, but the path cuts across grass, soil and boulder clay masking the next limestone bed down. Eventually it rises to a patch of white clints at the Middle Washfold Cave entrance; streams draining from the higher shale flow through deep fissures before finding a lower bedding plane and running into caves. None of these can be followed far without crawling, though the passages do go through the 900 m to Great Douk. Continue towards the wall and pass by another sinkhole on the left, most distinctive for a magnificently fluted limestone block which has also been undercut by erosion of a bedding plane. Cross the wall on the stile, and then go right over the next stile to keep to drier ground on the limestone right of the wall, away from the wetter shale slopes. The next stile carries the main path up Ingleborough, an energetic but worthwhile extension to the walk, but to keep to the limestone, just head along the contours to Sunset Hole where another stream sinks into a narrow cave entrance.

Beyond Sunset Hole there is no well-marked path, and the next wall is a major boundary wall. There is normally a good crossing point, for round-Ingleborough walkers, and this gives access to Meregill Hole. The name describes this most unusual pothole – it is a long rift with vertical walls cut in the limestone dropping 15 m to a deep lake – the Mere. When the stream pours into the Mere, its level rises and the exit is under water; but when the stream is diverted (now a permanent feature) the Mere drops to reveal the outlet at the south end into a magnificent cave. It was mainly explored between 1908 and 1912 in a series of famous sieges – needed in those days of such inadequate equipment. The streamway descends a succession of three great shafts each 25–35 m deep. Horrendous stories of men, dressed only in tweeds, being lowered on tarred ropes down these cascades, with candles for illumination, are still classics in the annals of cave exploration. They were hard men indeed who fought those conditions, and it is still a serious descent for the modern well-equipped caver. The staircase of shafts, and the huge rifts in between, head straight back into the hill following a major fault in the limestone. Only at a depth of 130 m does the stream find bedding planes and head north down dip in a splendid canyon streamway. This ends at a sump from where only flooded passages continue to the resurgence of God's Bridge. Meregill is certainly a place to ponder from the relative comfort of the moor.

West of Meregill there are some extensive pavements of excellent quality – well worth a diversion for anyone wanting to see unusually large unbroken slabs of the bare limestone. But then retrace the route past Sunset Hole and stop awhile beside Braithwaite Wife Hole. This enormous conical doline is 60 m in diameter and nearly 30 m deep. There is rock on one side but most of its slopes are slumped boulder clay. It appears to be a large preglacial sinkhole related to a complex of rifts and chambers beneath its floor (only accessible through the streamway of Sunset Hole), and it was blocked and partly filled when Ice Age glaciers overran it and left behind the boulder clay. It is still one of the largest depressions, or dolines, in the Dales and must have been even more impressive before the glaciers did their damage.

Continue north on the path between bare dry limestone pavements on the left and a boulder clay cover supporting ponds on the right. The path winds through more pavement and then opens out to a grassy hollow. Leave the main path and head across right towards a low rock scar which has a stone cairn on its left end. Scramble the few metres up on to the scar, and there in front lies perhaps the finest of Ingleborough's limestone pavements. Swing round to the right a bit to see the best of this dramatic rock landscape. Imagine the glaciers which swept down from the north plucking away the overlying beds, and scouring the surface to this strong slab of limestone. The ice retreated 14,000 years ago, but since then soil and vegetation have hardly stood a chance on the bare stone. Only rainwater has carved the surface by simple solution of the limestone, opening up the joints and etching the grooves which feed into them. Lichens however have thrived; they cover nearly all the surfaces and account for the rounded sculpting, as opposed to the sharp-edged channels which rain would have cut without their presence. In the Yorkshire Dales the rock slabs are

The clints at Middle Washfold, with Ingleborough rising beyond

known as clints, and the fissures as grykes, but the latter have
infinite variety in their grooves, hollows and miniature potholes.

Descend off the edge of the pavement before the next wall, to
rejoin the main path with its line of stiles back to the road. The
Great Douk area has so much to offer and must provide one of the
best of all walks in classic limestone country. The surface has a
variety of sinkholes, shafts and dolines, together with the excellent
pavements, while underground there are long stream caves. Even
these are on different levels – shallow in Great Douk and deep in
Meregill – so combining to create the three-dimensional complexity
that is true limestone karst.

The walk is on public footpaths to and from Sunset Hole, but there
may be no access to Meregill Hole.

8 – Twistleton Scars   705749

In all the Yorkshire Dales the longest line of unbroken limestone scars is at Twistleton, forming the north rim of Chapel le Dale just above Ingleton. In bright sunlight they are a magnificent sight with white limestone terraced up 150 m of the hillside, and individual scars creating vertical walls 30 m high. During the last Ice Age, a powerful glacier moved south between Ingleborough and Whernside; it deepened Chapel le Dale, it trimmed Twistleton Scars and it scoured the pavements of Scales Moor; the result is an impressive landscape.

The starting point for a circular walk is the old road along the north side of Chapel le Dale, reached from Ingleton by an ignominious route past the village gas-holder. Beyond Beezleys Farm, cars can be left on grass verges beside the road. There is a fine view across the dale to White Scar Cave and the limestone benches above it, and then over their crest to the Ingleborough summit; the quarries on either side, both working valuable roadstone, are an unwelcome but unavoidable intrusion. A signposted path heads up the hill and round the back of Twistleton Hall. It joins a lane, and shortly after the tar comes to an end a green track cuts obliquely up the hillside. This is the remains of a track once used to remove rockery stone from the limestone pavements above; fortunately that practice has now ceased, but it has left an easy route up the slope of Scar End.

At the top of the first rise there is a fine view back. The Craven Lowlands stretch out towards Morecambe Bay, and both left and right there is a marked step up on to the limestone plateau of the Craven Uplands. It is easy to see how the Craven Faults have so dominated the landscape by controlling the position of this great step; the faults constitute a major break in the bedrock geology and the limestone has been displaced far beneath the surface of the Craven Lowlands. The track continues but swings to the left, so, by the lone tree, cut across to the right aiming for the wall which scores the horizon. This way crosses a zone of conspicuously sliced limestone, marking the line of another minor fault, and then rises on to a low scar.

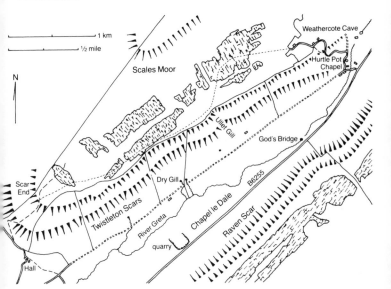

Twistleton Scars and Chapel le Dale

Scales Moor opens up ahead in an expansive view with the Whernside ridge seen end-on in the distance, and there is a choice of routes across this almost trackless plateau. To the right, the very substantial dry-stone wall follows the lip of Twistleton Scars, but there are fine views down into Chapel le Dale and across to the matching limestone crags of Raven Scar. Above them the grassy slopes rise steeply on the summit mass of Ingleborough; this is formed of the Yoredale Series shales and sandstones, but a thin limestone can be seen by its line of white scars just below the summit. Don't keep too close to the wall for across to the left are some impressively large expanses of limestone pavement. Scraped clean by Ice Age glaciers, but left dotted with rounded gritstone boulders carried there by the ice, these pavements are the hallmark of Yorkshire's limestone country. Rainwater solution of the joints has formed deep fissures and left many rocking blocks, so it is often

The sweeping pavements of Scales Moor

easier to walk on the grass between the pavement areas.

A shallow dry valley feeds through the wall and down the scars as Ullet Gill. Let this be the marker for a wide loop across to the left, for there lie more limestone pavements which are probably the finest in the country. Huge white slabs slope gently down to the east. They are broken only by widely-spaced fissures and just a scatter of glacial erratics – the rounded grit boulders. Similar landscapes in the French Alps are referred to as deserts – a fitting name for this panorama of rock almost devoid of vegetation. Some of the fissures and fluted potholes are many metres deep. The surface is dry, but water from the shale slopes nearby almost always runs through the fissures, heard but not seen until it finds its way into deeper caves.

The pavements should not be missed, but then head across a low grassy ridge which is formed by a tongue of boulder clay, aiming for the conspicuous white wall of the distant Hill Inn. In the distance to the left, the famous Ribblehead viaduct carries the railway across the broad valley down which came the Ice Age glacier. At the first dry-stone wall, keep left to find a gate on to a walled track, which is the way down to the valley floor – though a steeper path cuts off one corner. Turn right at the junction where the track joins another just above the rocky valley of Chapel Beck which is normally dry. The main valley river is here underground, flowing through a complex series of mainly flooded, and only partly explored, caves as far as the God's Bridge resurgence. An obvious large hole, ringed by trees just below the track, is Hurtle Pot. It is a gloomy place with dark muddy walls dropping into a black pool about 10 m in diameter. There is no obvious flow but it is connected to the main underground river, and the water level therefore fluctuates; it is normally some 10 m down. As it is in effect a hole in the roof of the flooded cave, divers use it to explore what lies below, and a rope guideline marks their route into the murky depths.

Beside the tiny chapel of St Leonard's, the track joins the old Chapel le Dale road which can probably be traced back to Roman origins. There is little alternative to a walk back down this road, but it is pleasant enough as almost all the traffic follows the main road on the other side of the valley. For much of the way it is unfenced, and the turf provides easier walking. It does give splendid views of the white limestone crags – Raven Scar across to the left, and Twistleton Scars above to the right. Individual beds of the limestone create grassy terraces within the staircase of Twistleton Scars, and these can provide some good walking except that gateless walls climb the entire slopes and obstruct any continuous routes. A spring line almost follows the road and marks the base of the limestone, best seen at Dry Gill which is a flood resurgence just a few metres down-valley from a permanently active rising. The Dry Gill cave has only a small entrance, above which lie the nearly-level beds of limestone; just below, the streambed is cut through almost vertical ribs of the much older slate and greywacke (the greywacke is the type of hard sandstone, and is the material being quarried for roadstone across the valley). From Dry Gill it is not far down the road to the starting point for this circular walk.

Twistleton Scars are a fine set of limestone crags, seen by many en route through Chapel le Dale. But few realise that, above them, Scales Moor has an even more spectacular landscape. The area is well worth a good walk and the high-level section has the added benefit of splendid views.

This whole route is on public paths and roads, except across the high moorland where there is no restriction on walkers.

9 – Weathercote Cave   739776

For more than 200 years Weathercote Cave has been one of the natural curiosities drawing visitors to the Yorkshire Dales. It is an impressively large waterfall shaft which received glowing descriptions in the writings of some of the earliest tourists to the region.

The cave lies right in the floor of the Chapel le Dale valley in the section just below the Hill Inn where the beck disappears and reappears at a number of places. Weathercote House is splendidly sited and across its front garden the dry valley of Chapel Beck is a swathe of grass; the cave lies in a walled enclosure and announces its presence by the roar of its waterfall. Through the one doorway in the wall, the path leads directly to the open hole with a flight of steps dropping down beneath a natural rock bridge. A terrace on the left extends over the bridge and gives the best view down the shaft. The surface opening is 60 m long and 10 m wide with vertical walls of moss-covered limestone. At the far end a powerful cascade drops 20 m to the floor of the shaft.

Across the rift just in front of the waterfall, a massive wedged boulder has always been known as Mohammed's Coffin, and behind it, the water emerges from a tall cave passage. The main Chapel Beck sinks some distance further up the dale and flows through caves to this point – though the passages are mostly low and wide and cannot be followed far because of the quantities of water. At

The hidden waterfall in Weathercote Cave

Weathercote, the cave finds a major cross joint and that is why the water cascades down the shaft, fortunately open to daylight and providing a most impressive sight.

Down the steps beneath the rock bridge, a slippery scramble leads to the foot of the shaft. In wet weather this is a maelstrom of wind and spray, but in drier conditions a small chamber can be reached under the left wall. The water drops through boulders and is not easily followed, but the passage below is only short before the beck enters a deep pool, next to see daylight at the God's Bridge resurgence, a kilometre down the valley. In conditions of high flood, the Weathercote shaft gains another waterfall from the normally dry, upstream, riverbed. And the downstream passages must be constricted, for the water may back up till it fills the shaft and overflows down the valley past the house (this happens only once or twice a year).

Providing a brief glimpse of an underground river, Weathercote Cave fully justifies its description as a window into the karst. And the waterfall makes it one of the more spectacular shafts in the Yorkshire limestone. Unfortunately there is some loose rock in the fractured walls, and the site is currently not open to the casual visitor. It has been included in this guide however because it was one of the first show caves in Yorkshire, has enthralled many tourists over more than two centuries, and there is every hope that it will, one day in the future, again be open for visitors.

The cave is in the private grounds of Weathercote House, and there is currently no access to it.

10 – White Scar Cave   713745

Around the eastern tip of Ingleborough the terraced crags of limestone have been known since time immemorial as White Scars. They rise high above the grassy slopes which fall away to Ingleton and the Craven Lowlands. Northwards they merge into Raven Scar to form half the splendid panorama of limestone which flanks both sides of Chapel le Dale. They have also given their name to the cave which opens at their foot – White Scar Cave.

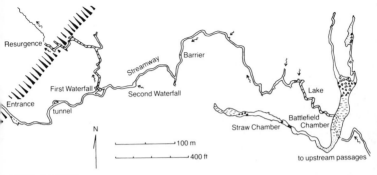

White Scar Cave

Across the dale from the cave entrance, Twistleton Scars expose the full thickness of the nearly level limestone, while the valley floor is cut into lower and older slates. Therein lies the origin of White Scar Cave, for it is a resurgence system draining the groundwater out of the limestone where it meets the impermeable slates. The show cave path enters through a dry passage, abandoned by the stream except for overflow in extreme floods. Originally this was a low passage, negotiated only by flat-out crawling, and part of it can be seen, just as the explorers found it, in a loop immediately inside the entrance. Discovered in 1923, White Scar was soon recognised as a potential show cave, and miners from the old Ingleton coalfield blasted the crawlway to turn it into the walking-height tunnel of today. The natural passage is a geological classic, formed right along the contact of the beds with a limestone roof and a slate floor; the boundary can still be seen along the first part of the cave, first near roof level then nearer the floor.

The sound of falling water heralds the junction with the active streamway, and the show cave route meets it at the foot of the First Waterfall. The stream drops about 2 m into a shallow pool and then flows off into a low tunnel on the left. This is the start of the very aqueous passages, only explorable in drought conditions, which the water follows to its exit into Chapel le Dale beside a small reservoir. These passages are so low because their floor is slate, resistant to erosion by the cave water. The stream only meets the slate at the foot of the First Waterfall where it cascades over the lowest few beds of limestone. Upstream of there, the whole 6 km of explored cave are entirely in the limestone, mostly well above the underlying slate. Because of the complexities of both geology and hydrology, a natural cave rarely fits the over-simplified textbook concept of groundwater flow along the base of the limestone, and White Scar is no exception.

At the top of the waterfall the passage is low, but the show cave path by-passes it in a tunnel, and then rejoins the streamway. From there on the cave is entirely natural, and is certainly a splendid example of active cave, alive with the stream which carved it and which is still enlarging it. The path has been built right beside the water, or bridged across it. At first the roof is rather low and the visitor has to stoop a little; the walls of wet limestone echoing the noise of the stream help to create the raw atmosphere of power and underground erosion. Suddenly the roof lifts, where the Second Waterfall is a tributary stream cascading into a small chamber, with calcite flowstone draped down the walls.

Upstream, the cave is a winding canyon more than 5 m tall. The path rises to clear a noisy ladder of cascades, and at one point the stream can be seen swirling through milled-out scour pools cut into the dark limestone. The gradient eases off, and the passage widens where flowstone banks line the walls, stalagmites stand along the ledges and thin stalactites hang from the roof. It is a very well decorated section of cave with some of the stalagmites stained by minerals, mainly iron compounds, and much of the flowstone terraced into micro-gour pools – many of the formations are still alive with dripping water. The roof is an almost level bedding plane in the limestone, and in a few places the visitor can see some spectacular fossil burrows left by animals that dug through the sea floor oozes before they crystallised into the limestone. While those animals and the limestone date back about 330 million years, the cave is less than one million years old. A stalagmite from the streamway has been dated to 225,000 years old, showing that the cave at least predates the last two Ice Ages when glaciers advanced down Chapel le Dale.

Calcite straws in the far reaches of White Scar Cave

The show cave path ends at the Barrier, with a splendid last view
of the stream passage. Tantalisingly the walls curve into the
darkness, to hide what lies beyond. Cavers have explored the
streamway for another 2 km; most of this length is along tall narrow
canyons, but a number of deep lakes and canals with very cold water
add to the excitement of the underground journey. The furthest
point reached is a totally submerged passage which lies about 80 m
directly below the floor of Crina Bottom. This sheltered limestone
valley lies on the main route from Ingleton to the summit of
Ingleborough, and walkers can hardly fail to notice the main stream
sinking into limestone rifts right beside the path. Partly blocked by
inwashed glacial debris, the intervening passages let the water
through but have so far failed all attempts at their full exploration.

High-level passages lie above the White Scar streamway, some of them famous for their spectacular groups of straw stalactites. Perfectly formed, each just the diameter of the drops of dripping water, these most fragile of calcite decorations are truly beautiful, fortunately protected from any damage by their inaccessibility. Above a massive boulder choke within the streamway lies a segment of high-level passage which enlarges into the Battlefield Chamber. This too is well decorated with straws but is more remarkable for its size – over 80 m long and 20 m wide. Long, long ago, before the main Ice Ages, it carried the underground river of Chapel le Dale. Today it is dry and silent except for the steady drip of the seepage water which continues to decorate it.

There is a possibility that the Battlefield Chamber could one day be part of an extended show cave, which would be on a spectacular scale. Though this is an exciting concept, the high costs of the access tunnels make it only a plan for the unspecified future. The other great attraction of White Scar Cave is its streamway, unmatched in any of Britain's other show caves. For a real feeling of underground erosion, and to see a cave actually being carved out of the rock, White Scar is well worth a visit.

The show cave is open daily throughout the year.

11 – Kingsdale 705785

In geological terms, Kingsdale is a classic. Its straight, clean glaciated trough is lined with limestone scars which overlook a flat floor of alluvium – sediment that accumulated in the ancient lake once dammed behind the terminal moraine at Raven Bay. And besides the textbook glacial features, Kingsdale has so many caves and potholes. It is one of the less frequented dales. The road, once busy with coal carts from the Ingleton collieries to the Dentdale mills, is now just a narrow backwater, only tarred over the pass in 1952. A walk on the limestone bench on the west side covers the best of the landscape, and is always away from the crowds.

Along the road, count three walls from the Braida Garth turn-off

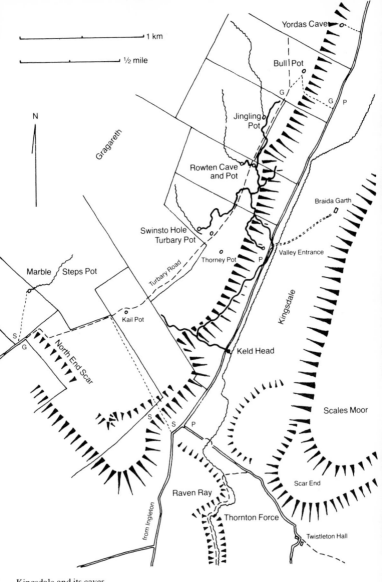

Kingsdale and its caves

and park a car in the double lay-by close to a gate on the left. Yordas Cave is even further up the valley but there is no high-level footpath from it. So, through the gate head straight up the field to the left end of the white crags of Shout Scar, and once over the scar head right for the tree at the entrance of Bull Pot. Iron sheeting prevents sheep falling down the shaft – a 12 m drop in a long dark rift between polished walls; water can be heard below, flowing from a sink in a parallel rift just up the fell. Bull Pot is only the first of dozens of potholes which drain to the Keld Head resurgence, though in only a few cases have cavers managed to follow the passages right through.

From Bull Pot, contour to the south and then join the green track of the Turbary Road through the gate in the wall. Centuries ago this road was used by peat cutters who followed it from Masongill up on to the fell bogs above the limestone bench. Now it is a convenient trail, close to the limestone boundary and passing all the main potholes. Through the gate look out over the ridge on the right for the tree which marks the site of Jingling Pot. The tree actually overhangs the shaft and, approached carefully, it gives a marvellous view straight down the 43 m of wet, polished, vertical walls – one of the more beautiful Yorkshire potholes. Part of the Jingling stream misses the pot and disappears into a low cave, which follows bedding planes in the limestone as far as Rowten Pot.

Along the road and through the next gate, Rowten Pot can hardly be missed. It is a massive rift feature over 40 m long picked out on major joints. At the north end it is 20 m deep to the stream cascading over ledges round a pile of collapse blocks, but it is deeper beneath a rock bridge. Tread warily round the Eyehole at the south end – it is a clear drop of 65 m; rockbolts on the walls are used by cavers to anchor their ropes when they go down the shaft then through the cave system to emerge close to the valley floor. Over by the Turbary Road, a rock window reveals the stream flowing into the pot, and the main sink is just over the rise to the west. Rowten Cave is wide open and visitors with just a torch can walk or paddle down the clean stream passage, though crawls and then cascades block the way to the Pot for all but equipped cavers. An upstream tributary can be followed through a smaller cave to another entrance.

Jingling Pot from below

Further south the Turbary Road is on a wide bench, with a line of sinkholes and shakeholes marking the limestone/shale boundary over to the right. One of these entrances is Swinsto Hole with its fine passages into the main system below. Beside the road, Turbary Pot is a rift 5 m deep, though it leads almost directly to the lip of a 35 m shaft, and just beyond it a flood streambed ends in narrow fissures in the bedrock. Over to the left Thorney Pot is a single blind shaft of 15 m; long ago it swallowed a stream but now it is dead, fossilised as erosion stripped the shale back to the modern line of sinks. It stands on the edge of pavements and scars with views down to the floor of Kingsdale, all relics of Ice Age glaciers.

Back on the Turbary Road, continue beside the wall, with increasingly good views across Scales Moor to White Scars and Ingleborough. Kail Pot is in a little valley left of the road; its wide 10 m deep shaft is slowly being filled with rubbish – a case of landscape desecration so sad to find in a National Park. Through the next gate, a path heads left back to Kingsdale, but it is worth continuing round to see Marble Steps Pot. The green track eventually steepens down North End Scar, and through the road gate, a stile on the right starts a path across the fell. It is not well marked, but head for the stand of trees which surround the pot, and on the way pass three spectacularly large dolines. These conical hollows have formed in the glacial sediment as it has slumped into fissures in the underlying limestone, and a rubble heap in one is evidence of the efforts of cavers trying to clear the fissures to gain access to caves beneath.

In contrast, Marble Steps Pot has a massive entrance. A major stream has carved an inclined tunnel over 5 m in diameter down through a series of joints. Today the water, when it flows, sinks a few metres back up the beck, leaving dry this giant's staircase of polished limestone. A very careful scramble down a gully on the left leads to an impressive vantage point on the edge of the main drop. Beware the slippery rock, for the rock steps continue down a total of 60 m. They end in a chamber, though further passages have been explored by cavers till they reach pools of water at the same level as the Keld Head resurgence.

Return over North End Scar and take the path to the south-east, across a succession of limestone pavements separated by low scars. Far ahead the profile of Ingleborough distinguishes the line of the Craven Fault, where the main limestone beds are abruptly truncated to overlook the downfaulted shales of the Craven Lowlands. Close to hand, the Cheese Press Stone is a glacial erratic of more massive limestone carried by ice from up the dale, and below it the path descends steeply beside a succession of scars in more broken, faulted limestone. Follow the road back along the floor of Kingsdale; there is so little traffic that it is still a good walk, and it does pass two more important caves.

Keld Head is the first, just below the road and reached over a convenient stile. It appears as a wide shallow pool, but a considerable flow emerges from beneath the rock wall; it is the single resurgence for the water sinking into all the potholes on both sides of Kingsdale. Cave-divers have explored 3 km of submerged passages, and have connected it to the main cave system below Rowten Pot. The riverbed along Kingsdale is dead straight where it has been canalised to prevent flooding of the fields; it is only active in wet weather for its water normally sinks at various places near the top of the dale and finds its way through the caves to Keld Head. Opposite the Braida Garth turning, Valley Entrance appears as an oil drum set in the hillside. An opening through the cover of soil and glacial debris was dug out by cavers to give access to the passage in the limestone just below; now it is the most popular route into the extensive cave system on this side of Kingsdale, even if its entry is a little ignominious.

Within that cave the main stream to Keld Head can be found flowing when the surface channel down the valley floor is dry. Kingsdale is an excellent example of underground drainage, where the caves are the main arteries and only excess floodwater stays on the surface across the limestone.

The caves are all on private land, but there is no restriction on reasonable access to them and along the Turbary Road.

12– Thornton Force   692760

At the southern end of Kingsdale, the river emerges from Keld
Head and maintains a surface course all the way out to the Craven
Lowlands and eventually Morecambe Bay. On its way down to
Ingleton it drops over an impressive sequence of waterfalls; the
finest of these is the top one, Thornton Force, also the only one on
limestone and a fascinating geological locality.

Leave the Kingsdale road, where there is room to park a few cars
at the junction, on the green track which heads south-east across the
dale. There is a footbridge over the river, and then a rise to where a
path heads back to the left through a kissing gate. From the field
there is a good view of Raven Ray, the grassy barrier which almost
blocks the mouth of Kingsdale. It is probably England's finest
example of a terminal moraine – a mass of debris and sediment
dumped by the melting ice when the Kingsdale glacier reached just
to here for a time during its final retreat at the end of the last Ice
Age. The moraine completely blocked the old valley, and meltwater
from the receding glacier formed a lake behind it – hence the flat
sediment floor of Kingsdale. Eventually the lake overtopped the
moraine and was drained as the river cut its present channel a little
to the east of the old valley line. Follow the path down to the
footbridge and then alongside this youthful channel.

Thornton Force is first seen from the top where the river drops
past some large slabs of limestone, but the path continues round.
From below it is a fine sight, with the water dropping a sheer 14 m.
It is a classic 'Niagara-type' waterfall, with a lip of strong rock (the
limestone) overlying a weaker rock (the slate) in which the plunge
pool is carved. The resultant overhang even provides a sheltered
path behind the cascade, and this gives a close-up view of the
unconformity between the vertical slate and the horizontal
limestone. Stand and think for a moment how the slate was formed,
metamorphosed and folded, and then had its top eroded away many
millions of years before its surface sank beneath the sea where the
limestone beds were deposited on top. Look for the boulders in the

Thornton Force

lowest limestone bed – remnants of the beach sediments formed as the slate was slowly overrun by the sea, 330 million years ago.

Just to the left of the Force, a much smaller waterfall drops from a cave almost on to the path. Some of this water is leakage from the riverbed upstream; the flow of the river is too great to let it all sink underground, but a river always tries to form a cave in limestone country. Then from a few hundred metres downstream of the Force, look back; see how the limestone crag just above the path is matched by the rocks beside the waterfall – but is missing across the end of the valley: there, the grassy slopes cover the Raven Ray moraine where it plugs the old, buried, valley. Thornton Force has been created where the river found its way past the moraine barrier and dropped back into its original valley, though it has worn its way back into the hillside perhaps 60 m in the 14,000 years since it first found this route.

Downstream the path continues past the staircase of cascades known as Pecca Falls, all carved in the bands of vertical grit and slate well below the limestone. Only Swilla Glen, even further downstream, is cut in limestone where a slice of it is brought to river level between the great dislocation surfaces of the North and South Craven Faults. And then the limestone is lost altogether way beneath the surface of the Craven Lowlands.

Many visitors to the dales make the popular Waterfalls Walk. Traditionally this starts at Ingleton, where there is an appropriately large car park, and goes up Swilla Glen, then past Pecca Falls and Thornton Force. It then loops south-east along the green track past Twistleton Hall and returns past the Beezley and Snow Waterfalls – but the River Greta is at a lower level and all of its falls are in the slate and grit beneath the limestone.

Whether Thornton Force is the highlight of the Waterfalls Walk, or an extension of a visit to Kingsdale, it never fails to impress. Well-known to many geologists, it is worth anyone's time as it tells so much of the Dales' prehistory, both thousands and millions of years ago.

The lower part of the Waterfalls Walk is on private ground, and a small charge is made at the kiosk at the Ingleton end.

13 – Yordas Cave   706791

Taking its name from a legendary Norse giant, Yordas Cave is of a size perhaps befitting a giant's residence. Even though relatively isolated at the top end of Kingsdale, the cave was one of the better-known sights of Yorkshire to the earliest genuine tourists who roamed the uplands of Britian a couple of centuries ago. Into Victorian times Yordas was known as a show cave, but it never gained any fixed lighting and progressively fell into disuse, so that today it is in an almost undisturbed state.

The cave is easily found as it lies in the only large stand of trees on the western side of the broad flat-floored section of Kingsdale. There's a convenient lay-by on the road just below it. Through the gate, keep right of the valley and a path heads straight into a rocky ravine overshadowed by the high trees. This small limestone gorge is cut into the steepest section of slope flanking the glaciated trough of Kingsdale. It no longer carries a surface stream as it was formed long ago at the end of the Ice Ages when the caves were blocked by sediment and ground ice. Today, Yordas Gill sinks up near the top of the limestone and flows through the cave which lies just beside and almost beneath the abandoned gorge.

Below the rock wall on the left, a few steps lead down to the stone-built arch which frames the entrance. The arch once held a door, and the entrance is now rather lower than it was in the past; a rockfall and a mass of flood debris raised the floor of the gorge during a monumental storm in 1817. Immediately inside the cave widens. It has a floor of compact mud, and an irregular roof low enough in parts to catch an unwary head. Tread carefully until eyes have adjusted to the gloom, and follow the right-hand wall. In just a few metres the mudbank slopes down to the stream and the roof disappears upwards. At first the Main Chamber seems unfathomable; its size is magnified by the darkness which unadjusted eyes cannot yet penetrate. In fact it is somewhere over 10 m high and wide and about 45 m long. The floor is gravel and cobbles washed by the shallow stream between low mudbanks, and the roof at the upper end is a flat bedding plane bearing a lacework of small stalactites along the fracture lines. More joints guide the clean vertical walls.

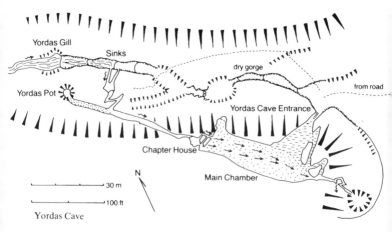

Yordas Gill

Sinks

dry gorge

from road

Yordas Pot

Yordas Cave Entrance

Chapter House

Main Chamber

N

├────────┤ 30 m

├────────┤ 100 ft

Yordas Cave

Downstream to the left, the roof becomes lower and the water
runs off into a low passage. The outlet is constricted by a massive
boulder choke, marked on the surface by a collapsed depression in
the wood. There is a low, 'grovelly' route out to another entrance,
but the water sinks into fissures, next to be seen in the Kingsdale
Master Cave and then returning to daylight at Keld Head. In very
wet weather the water backs up and turns the whole chamber into a
lake.

To the right, upstream, the chamber is larger, and the roof soars
up a high aven at the top end. Follow the sound of water and head
for the top left-hand corner of the chamber. Then step through a
couple of rock arches, the second cut through flowstone, into the
Chapter House. Here the entire stream crashes down a broken
waterfall from a passage 10 m above, and drains out through a
narrow rift. It is an impressive shaft, with the walls draped in calcite
flowstone, and in wet weather is a maelstrom of wind and spray.
Retreat to the main chamber and now that eyes are adjusted, its size
can be appreciated. It has a complex origin. It dates back a few
hundred thousand years when it was dissolved out of the limestone
by water which filled it to the roof, before Kingsdale was there to
drain it away. The close jointing of the rock caused wall and roof

The main chamber of Yordas Cave

collapse to give it the square profile. Then the climatic variations of the Pleistocene Ice Ages saw it filled with sediment and re-excavated a number of times; witness the fragments of cobble beds and stalagmite floors now stuck high on the walls of the chamber.

Return to daylight, and take a little path which climbs the rock scar almost opposite and heads up between the trees just above the rock ravine. The path crosses the dry streambed just below a miniature limestone gorge where the stream can be seen cascading down the upper end. Scramble up the dry section, and the water can be seen dropping into polished fissures opened on vertical joints which cross the streambed. The two main fissures unite inside; the stream drops down another waterfall and then flows along an almost level passage to the top of the Chapter House waterfall. It can be followed through by cavers, but the route is very wet and hardly worth the ladders and changes of clothes.

Back on the main path, ascend the grass bank above the sinkholes and Yordas Pot lies between a number of trees both standing and fallen. It is a narrow rift in bedrock exposed in a depression below about a metre of soil cover. Jammed tree trunks make it safe to stand right over the entrance; it bells out into a fine circular shaft 22 m deep, washed by a stream emerging from a side fissure and dropping into blackness. Until 1963 the entrance did not exist. The shaft had been found from below, for it connects to the cave, but it had no daylight down it. Then in that year, a storm blew over a tree which had been rooted in soil right across the narrow top of the fissure – limestone country is full of surprises. The water falling down the shaft comes from shallow fissures fed from the main streambed. Limestone extends to just beyond the wall at the top of the woods, and Yordas Gill tumbles over a series of rock ledges into its youthful gorge before it finds the fissures which allow it to disappear underground.

With its streambed sinkholes, an open pothole, a miniature gorge and an accessible cave, Yordas Gill provides a microcosm of limestone landforms. It is particularly interesting to see the fossil surface course and the active underground course of a single stream so close together. The anomaly within the site is the size of the cave chamber, but that just makes a visit to Yordas all the more worth while.

The cave is on private land but the farmer does not restrict reasonable access.

14 – Swinsto Hole   694775

Beneath the western benches of Kingsdale, the caves form a remarkably well-integrated system. In the complex mazes of underground drainage routes, narrow, flooded or boulder-choked sections normally provide barriers to exploration; this is not so in West Kingsdale. Passages from three of the sinks high on the limestone fells can be followed down till they join and then lead out to entrances on the valley floor.

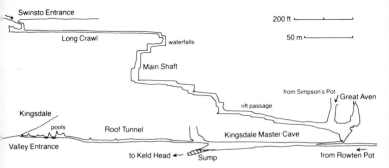

Cross section through Swinsto Hole and the Kingsdale Master Cave

Swinsto Hole is one of these three, and is deservedly the most
popular with cavers. It is a classic pothole, whose stream can be
followed down nine underground waterfalls in a clear-washed
passage cut in light cream and grey limestones. It was explored as
far as a boulder choke below the Great Aven in 1930, and it was
then reckoned to be one of the most arduous caves in the country.
This was mainly due to the loads of heavy rope ladder which had to
be carried down for the waterfalls. But today it is a joy to explore,
when only one rope is needed. Each waterfall can be safely abseiled
and the rope is then pulled down for use on the next drop. It is of
course a very committing way to descend a cave, only possible when
the route is known to a low-level exit, which also removes the effort
of climbing back up out of the cave.

The entrance to Swinsto is most insignificant, one in a line of little
shakeholes along the shale boundary at the back of the main
limestone bench. The first bit of passage is small too – a few metres
of crawl to a shaft which drops to the stream at the start of the Long
Crawl. This continues for 300 m and was the hard work of olden
days, but without a heavy load of tackle it is really very easy. It ends
at the second waterfall. And it is the next section of cave which
demonstrates so well the lure of the sport of cave exploration. Seven
cascades are so closely spaced that they almost form a staircase to
the depths. The stream always beckons onwards; the descent is

West Kingsdale Master Cave

exciting. There is enough water to keep the adrenalin flowing, but not enough to be really threatening. The waterfall shafts are all different; on some the water is safely to one side, on others the caver descends under its full force; some land on polished rock, some in deep pools. The main shaft is a landmark, fully 30 m deep with the rope descent broken at a spray-lashed ledge where the noise is one of the unforgettable features.

Below the waterfalls, the stream runs off into a tall rift passage, easy going for the caver, as far as a pair of soaring avens, the second being 50 m high. These are alternative routes in from the Simpson's Pot entrance. Below the second one, Great Aven, a route was found through the boulders only in 1966. A small passage continues, degenerates into a wide crawlway, and then breaks out on to a ledge in the Kingsdale Master Cave. A powerful stream sweeps through, carrying all the drainage from the north end of Kingsdale. Upstream, the only explorable route in is from Rowten Pot, but streams also come from Jingling Pot, Yordas Cave and the sinks of the main beck on the floor of the dale. Downstream, all the water races into a splendid canyon passage, with rock chutes, deep pools and rapids, twisting between polished walls.

All too soon, the Master Cave ends in a deep, black sump pool. From there to the Keld Head resurgence, the water flows through 2000 m of completely submerged passage which have been completely traversed by cave-divers – on what is one of the world's longest cave-diving explorations. For the normal caver, the way on is a hole in the wall, 7 m above the sump pool, which can be reached by various rope and climbing tactics. This is an abandoned tunnel, no longer used since the stream found a lower route. In the silence so typical of these fossil caves it is a rather featureless walk, with an unwelcome break provided by a pair of deep, very cold pools with only limited airspace. But that final chilling experience is almost in sight of daylight, reached by an ignominious crawl through an oil drum which stabilises the loose earth in the transition from solid rock to wide open space.

Valley Entrance is very close to the Kingsdale road. In a straight line, it is just 500 m from the Swinsto entrance, though the underground route loops well up the dale following the whims of the limestone geology and is 1400 m long. It took the streams of Kingsdale over a quarter of a million years to carve the caves; it takes the caver just a few hours to descend through them. Though Swinsto Hole may appeal mainly to the sporting caver, it is a vital component of the underground drainage which has stamped out the character of the Kingsdale landscape.

All the cave entrances are on private land, but the farmer does not restrict reasonable access.

15 – Lost Johns Cave   671786

Lying in the lee of the Great Coum and Gragareth hills, Leck Fell was protected from the powerful Ice Age glaciers sweeping down from the north. So it has none of the bare pavements or ice-trimmed scars which typify the limestone benches above the other dales further east. But the fell was covered by ice – a slow-moving icesheet which spread right over the hill summits, and which, when it melted away, left a thick blanket of boulder clay. Consequently the scenery of Leck Fell is one of bleak slopes with the glacial debris supporting a cover of heather and tussock grass. The only signs of limestone are the disappearing streams, the numerous holes which pockmark the fell, and the spectacular caves which lie beneath.

A narrow road from Leck village gives convenient access to the fell. It ends at the lonely farm of Leck Fell House, and not far below is a small car park which is well used by cavers nearly every weekend. Above the level of the car park, streams flow down the shale slopes of Gragareth, but they sink as soon as they find the limestone hidden beneath the boulder clay. The dominant feature of Leck Fell is the hundreds of shakeholes – conical depressions in the boulder clay where water, draining through to the limestone, has sapped the sediment from below, like the sand in an egg-timer.

There is also a handful of much larger shafts down into the limestone. Below the road, Rumbling Hole is an awesome drop of 40 m which takes its name from the noise of the waterfall which crashes down it after emerging from a tributary cave. Beyond the

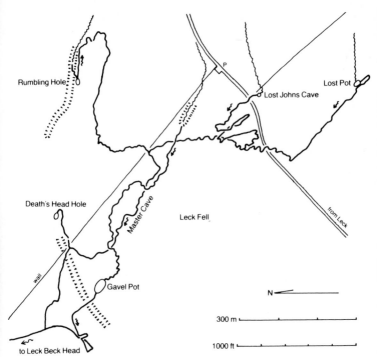

Lost Johns and the caves of Leck Fell

reach of daylight cavers can follow a succession of wet and noisy
shafts which unfortunately end in a sump pool too small to pass.
Nearer to the wall across the fell, Death's Head Hole is dry, silent
and deceptive – for it is 60 m deep down a beautiful cylindrical
shaft. Fossil passages lead off from its foot, and a tiny stream
disappears into a floor of boulders. Across the wall, Gavel Pot is an
elongated hole 30 m deep, and, as with the other two, sloping
boulder clay at its lip warrants caution in approaching it. Below the
Gavel entrance shaft there is a major stream passage; upstream it

The Master Cave of Lost Johns

extends to just a few metres from the sink below the car park, while downstream there are galleries decorated with stalagmites and then more deep shafts to a sump pool. Lost Pot, across the road, is a crater-like hole with a floor of boulders.

The least impressive entrance is the key to the caves of Leck Fell. Lost Johns Cave lies where a stream, just above the road, disappears into an entrance a little smaller than a doorway. It is the realm exclusively of the fully-equipped caver, but it is a splendid cave system. The stream has found its way into a complex of intersecting joints in the limestone, and over many thousands of years has cut and abandoned a succession of passages. There are three routes down for the caver, one of which still carries the stream; and each consists of easy horizontal passages connecting spacious cylindrical shafts. The three routes converge at the Wet Pitch – an aptly-named 20 m drop. In dry weather, the stream tinkles and rains down one side, but in wet weather the whole place vibrates under the hammering of the waterfall. The descent of Lost Johns ends where the stream passage twists round a last few bends, and then breaks through the wall of the Leck Fell Master Cave.

The Master Cave is the heart of the underground drainage beneath the fell. It is the main conduit to which all the other cave streams are tributaries. Every caver dreams of discovering his own master cave, and since this one was found in 1928 it has made Lost Johns one of the most popular caves in the Pennines. It extends for 2 km, winding beneath the surface 150 m above; for most of its length it is a few metres wide and over 5 m high, and it provides a delightfully easy underground walk which is a journey of exploration for every visitor.

Once in the Master Cave, it is clear that the Lost Johns stream is just another tributary. Upstream of the junction, the main cave continues through the high chamber of Lyle Cavern, before diminishing to a much smaller streamway which ends at the foot of the tall shafts bringing the water down from Lost Pot. Downstream the cave meanders around for 300 m before meeting another long tributary inlet which can be followed up to a sump frustratingly close to the lowest point accessible in Rumbling Hole. Even farther downstream the roof lowers, and though the passage continues to

be of walking height it has water neck-deep for 50 m through the
Long Pool. Fortunately for the chilled visitor, the pool does end,
where another tributary passage brings in the water from Death's
Head Hole, though it cannot be followed through the massive
boulder pile at the foot of the main shaft. Not far beyond that
junction the caver meets the sump pool. From there on the
submerged passage is only explorable by cave-divers, but they have
found the underwater junction with the Gavel Pot tributary.
Downstream the flooded cave continues, a serious exploration
challenge only now being probed by the divers, but eventually the
water returns to daylight at Leck Beck Head at the foot of the Ease
Gill valley.

   So the Master Cave collects all the drainage of Leck Fell – it is the
artery within the limestone. Lost Johns just happens to be the only
accessible entrance; but it is fortunate that it exists, for how else
could one even guess at the existence of that stream cave twisting its
way beneath the heather-covered moors of the windswept
Pennines?

Permission to descend the caves of Leck Fell is obtained through
the Council of Northern Caving Clubs.

16 – Ease Gill   663815

Even though it lies on the boundary of Cumbria and Lancashire, the
geology of Ease Gill means that it really is part of the Dales
limestone country. It is one of the lesser-visited limestone valleys,
though it is well known to cavers as it provides the scenic setting for
the entrances to Britain's longest cave system. The first road across
the beck is at Cowan Bridge, famed for its Brontë connections, but
there is an easy approach from Bullpot Farm, signposted off the
Roman road from Cowan Bridge to Barbon. The lane crosses a high
ridge from where there is a splendid view of Ease Gill, normally a
dry stony bed above the resurgence hidden in the wooden gorges at
the lower end. The farm is now a cavers' hut, but there is room to
park cars just above it; then walk down through the yard and right
through a gateway.

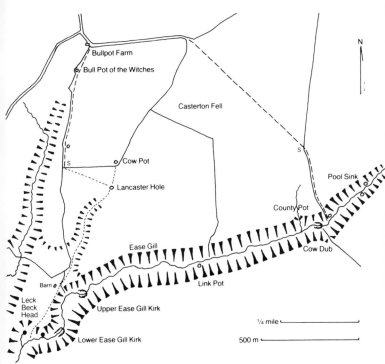

The surface around Ease Gill

Just down the track, Bull Pot of the Witches opens at the right – a 15 m deep shaft which can be seen by leaning with care round a tree right on its edge. It may be dry, or carrying a torrent of water, and a dark archway below is the way into a complex of cave passages. The track continues past a couple more, smaller, entrances to different parts of the cave system, while the valley on the right traces the line of the Dent Fault, beyond which the slate rocks contain no caves at all. Over the stile turn left across the moor to a shallow dry valley, where a group of rocks surrounds a pothole entrance guarded by an iron lid. This is Lancaster Hole, discovered in 1946 when a caver sat nearby and saw grass being blown about by a wind emerging through a chink in the rocks. With just a few boulders moved aside the 35 m shaft below gave the first route into the main cave system; further explorations still continue today.

A thin path up the shallow valley leads to Cow Pot, a complex shaft where a waterfall drops 20 m beside an impressively sharp needle of limestone. Continue the walk down the valley from Lancaster Hole. Curve left before the wall, then through the gate, go left of Hellot Barn and down the nose of the ridge to where Leck Beck Head lies just right of the valley junction. This is the resurgence for all the cave water under Leck and Casterton Fells but there is no accessible cave. So go left into Ease Gill itself and either walk up the dry bed of the beck, or in times of flood keep to a series of thin paths at higher levels which may require a degree of careful scrambling. The gill starts as a small gorge with a floor of polished limestone and, on the left, the dark mouth of Witches Cave. In wet weather it pours forth a torrent, but when dry can be followed a few metres to deep static pools which connect to the flooded caves at lower levels.

Upstream of Witches Cave the gill only carries a stream in the strongest flood, but deep pools deflect the walker on to a higher path as far as a wider section which immediately closes into the Lower Ease Gill Kirk. This rock amphitheatre is ringed by vertical walls 10 m high, cut by a notch where the streambed enters over a polished dry waterfall only 3 m high. This is not an easy climb, but a novel alternative is a cave entrance just to the right which leads to a narrow rift by-passing the obstacle. Daylight reaches most of the cave, just a few metres long, and though the first step up is a bit in the dark (a small torch can help) the clean rock walls are close enough to make the climb through both safe and easy. Above the underground section of path, there is more polished rock floor and then a daylight scramble to avoid the last few deep pools, before the valley opens out. But straight away, it closes into the Upper Kirk. An easy climb leads into the rock basin, where in wet weather a

Lower Ease Gill Kirk, with the way up through the cave on the right

powerful cascade drops into a deep pool and normally sinks into
Kirk Pot, a short but very flood-prone cave in the eastern bank.
There is no way up out of the Kirk, so by-pass it on a path up to the
right.

The next part of Ease Gill is a peaceful sheltered valley where the
main landmarks are the cave entrances, though none can be safely
entered without equipment. The most conspicuous is Link Pot, a
shored shaft 15 m deep on the eastern bank. It was found only in
1978 when a narrow fissure was enlarged by cavers, but it drops
straight into large dry passages which connect Leck and Casterton
Fells underground. It is a classic of limestone's unique drainage, so
that even when the gill carries a flood stream there is a dry route
through the caves beneath it. Upstream, Cow Dub is a deep pool,
with an underground outlet, ringed by vertical white walls, and a
stream may enter it through a narrow ravine long enough to cut
through the one strong bed of limestone. There is a path round to
the right.

Above Cow Dub, the gill is for 300 m a classic piece of limestone
valley – a miniature gorge flanked by rock scars and grassy terraces.
Within it there are 19 cave entrances, and various streams play
ducks and drakes at sinks and risings. In wet weather a beck flows
the length of the gill, but in dry conditions smaller streams rise from
the Leck Fell side and sink into the caves under Casterton Fell,
following the northerly dip of the limestone. County Pot is the
shored shaft on the rock terrace to the left and is the cavers' most
popular route into the main cave system. Round the corner the gill
is a miniature box canyon with a polished floor cut in limestone beds
rich in large brachiopod fossils. A perfectly round tube in the right
wall is aptly named the Borehole, and the canyon ends at a wide
shallow pool where a small entrance on the left, Pool Sink, again
leads to the main caves.

Beyond Pool Sink, Ease Gill opens out and soon loses the
limestone. So return to County Pot and take the stile above, on to
the path marked with stakes across the peat and bog of the moor; it
leads back to Bullpot Farm. It can be a wet walk over the moor, for
the limestone is buried by boulder clay, but down below there is a
rabbit warren of dry caves. Both above and below ground, Ease Gill

is a marvellous section of limestone country.

Ease Gill is all on private land, but this route follows concession paths established for access to the caves.

17 – Ease Gill Caverns   675805

An underground journey through the heart of the Ease Gill Caverns is the obvious complement to a visit to the sinkholes and gorges of the surface gill. The caves do however remain the strict preserve of the fully equipped caver. Though few parts of the very extensive system demand any seriously difficult caving, there are no walk-in entrances which can offer any potential for the casual visitor.

The caves of the Ease Gill system are really magnificent. They have every type of passage; narrow twisting streamways, powerful turbulent rivers, great waterfall shafts, vast silent caverns, and in addition some of the loveliest stalactite and stalagmite displays in the country. With more than 45 km of interconnected passages, there are currently only twelve cave systems known in the rest of the world which are longer. The complexity of the passages almost defies description – the cave map shows only half the story because it does not explain the many different levels of the passages, nor does it show the chaos of giant boulders which obscure so many of the junctions. In many parts of the system, route-finding is exceptionally difficult; it is particularly important that anyone making a traverse of the caves from one entrance through to another should do so in the company of someone who knows the cave well. No guidebook can hope to be adequate on its own. It is best to gain just a flavour of the Ease Gill Caverns by making some of the classic trips into parts of the system.

One of the most popular Ease Gill trips is in through the Country Pot entrance and up to Easter Grotto. With its entrance almost on the floor of the gill, County Pot consists of a series of stream canyons draining surface water northwards to join the underground river deep beneath Casterton Fell. Most of these streamways are

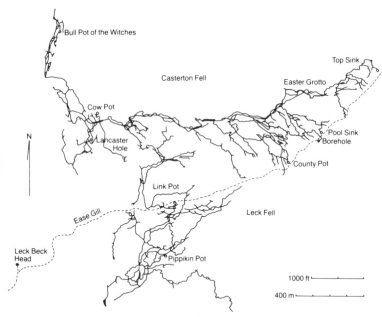

The cave system beneath Ease Gill

only a metre or so wide but perhaps 5 m tall. They twist and turn
between polished walls in the cream-coloured limestone. There are
junctions everywhere and even just following down the water is of
no help. The only passable route to the inner caverns joins and then
leaves three separate streams. But it's easy going, and there are only
two small waterfalls to be laddered before the explorer arrives at
Eureka Junction. The name of the junction reflects the excitement
of the first explorers who realised that they had at last found their
way into the underground river. A gallery 5 m wide extends both
ways with the clear water gliding over ribs of rock and through
shallow pools.

Upstream the passage is easy walking at first, but then becomes much larger and more complex. The broken roof rises to 20 m in places, and the walls are maybe 15 m apart, for the river here has broken into a much older complex of very large caverns. Gigantic boulders hinder progress along the floor; the water escapes through impassable cracks. Boulder slopes rear into the darkness of each side, and every other shadow hides the entrance to yet another gallery. There are three levels of passages; solid rock floors start with promise, but then end in black voids, the continuation far below or across the other side of an uncrossable chamber. But there is a way through this three-dimensional maze, and it continues into a fine stream canyon with clean rock, some good straw stalactites and none of the breakdown from the older passages. 400 m upstream there is a tall chamber, with a climb up the far wall straight into Easter Grotto.

First entered at Easter 1951, the Grotto is really just a segment of the old high-level passages. With the stream now in its new passage far below, Easter Grotto is dry, silent and timeless. It's only a few metres high, mostly about 5 m wide and perhaps 100 m long. Banks of clay line either side of a shallow trench, beneath a flat limestone roof. But since the stream abandoned it, water has dripped through the roof for thousands of years, and has created the most extraordinary display of stalactites and stalagmites. Individually they are not large, but the density of them is almost without parallel, and that short section of passage is one of the finest spectacles in the Pennines.

There is no simple explanation as to why Easter Grotto is so splendidly decorated. The passage is old, so there has been plenty of time for the calcite formations to be deposited; many other passages of similar age and level are also well decorated, but not as well as Easter Grotto. It is just that in this one passage all the interacting processes of geology and hydrology came together in the right way to permit the maximum amount of calcite deposition – somewhere had to be the best. The same complexity of cave development processes accounts for the maze and variety of passages in the Ease Gill system. For hundreds of thousands of years, streams coursed through the fractures, fissures and weaknesses in the limestone, each stream carving its own cave, and then abandoning it in

Easter Grotto

response to changes in drainage, climatic variations and the periodic
glaciations. Each change saw new caves, cutting through and linking
the old ones – and the end result is the caverns of today.

Variety and contrast are the essence of Ease Gill Caverns. They
are perhaps best appreciated on one of the many underground
traverses which can be made. From Cow Pot to Pippikin Pot is one
of the finest. It is very satisfying to go underground on Casterton
Fell and return to daylight on Leck Fell, having gone right beneath
the Ease Gill valley. The contrasts and variety of the caves along the
route are what make the traverse a caving classic, but would also
make a full description extremely long. Instead, just a taste of the
excitement from a whistle-stop trip.

Down Cow Pot on 15 m of ladder. A tight vertical slot and then a
low crawl following a tiny stream. Hole in the floor to blackness;

down 40 m of ladder through a rift in the roof of a massive chamber; spray and space, and far below a rocky floor. Scramble up the far wall, into silent sand-floored galleries meandering into darkness. A group of sparkling stalactites is the pointer to a narrow side rift. Climbing, squeezing, traversing along walls covered in a layer of dried mud. A dozen junctions, up into the roof, a wider gallery; some stalactites break the brown of the mud. Down a 30 m shaft, clean streamways, polished rock and easy walking. Just before a sump, an inlet; more walking, but upstream now. Another shaft, 30 m soaring upwards, the ladder left by friends coming the other way, and a good climb through the cold showerbath. Contortions through a boulder pile, then out into something like a railway tunnel.

Halfway now, this tunnel goes clean underneath Ease Gill. Too much clay on the floor; there is crawling ahead. A bit more water, it's a mudbath, flat-out squirming in thick brown porridge. It's narrow too; this section of crawl was dug through the soft clay by the cavers who, in 1978, made the traverse possible by linking the two halves of the cave system. It's larger beyond, with a sandy floor, through to the Hall of the Ten. Down a great boulder pile, blackness above and ahead, but a tiny hole in the floor beckons down to another streamway. Walking upstream, cleaner now too, up a 10 m shaft and through a decorated chamber. Then a difficult traverse, the rift tapering downwards, only minute sloping ledges to help keep up in the wide sections; this bit is hard work. A 2 m high waterfall, on a bend and in a passage so narrow that it is a serious obstacle. After that, the narrow bits which make Pippikin infamous. Five pleasant and roomy shafts each needing only a short ladder, but between them five diabolical squeezes in narrow rifts each less than 25 cm wide. The worst slopes upwards, has a bend in it and has no floor at the end. Each one a struggle, but then a source of amusement as friends struggle. Not a place for large people, and a challenge for all but midgets. But the fifth ladder leads straight up to daylight, the heather moors of Leck Fell, sunshine and warmth.

Spread all of that over six hours of sustained effort, shared with a small team of friends, and it makes an unforgettable experience.

Permission to visit the Ease Gill Caverns is obtained through the Council of Northern Caving Clubs.

18 – Hutton Roof and Newbiggin Crags 571784

West of the Pennine fells, the Lancashire Plain extends across to the rim of Morecambe Bay. It is lowland farming country, softly contoured from clays and sandstones plastered with a veneer of glacial debris. The line of the plain is however broken by two hills, each a block of limestone bounded by faults – Hutton Roof Crags and, adjacent to its north side, Farleton Knott. The main features of both hills are their limestone pavements; they are spectacular examples which attract geographers and geologists from far and wide. Standing square in the Lancashire Plain, the hills took the full force of the Ice Age glaciers moving south from the Lake District. Stripped clean of soil and overburden, the pavements survive today modified only by the patterns of post-glacial solution.

Start from Hutton Roof, a hamlet on the east side of the crags. The road is wide enough to park cars, and almost opposite the road junction a stony track leads between two houses and up the hill. Through a gate the path curves left, then swings back up the hill, just right of a standing stone and up a bracken-covered slope, following a natural break known as Blasterfoot Gap. Left of the path, the hillside has a distinctive saw-tooth profile in a small area known as The Rakes. Beds of limestone slope up steeply to almost vertical scars which drop down to the next bed. Turn left along the first ridge for the finest view across the bare inclined slabs.

The Rakes were formed by the glaciers moving across them from the north. Instead of just smoothing over the hill profile, great wedges of rock were torn out by the ice, in each case down to a weakness provided by the inclined bedding planes. The next bed of limestone was then left by the ice with a clean top surface, broken only by a diamond-shaped pattern of joints. After deglaciation, rainwater widened the joints to form the grykes visible today, but water also trickled over the inclined slabs in between. This trickling water slowly dissolved long, parallel grooves, known by the German word 'karren', each groove becoming wider and deeper further down the slab until it ends where the water drained into a gryke. Rainwater still flows in them today but the deepening process is slow indeed. These spectacular sloping karren are on a scale unmatched

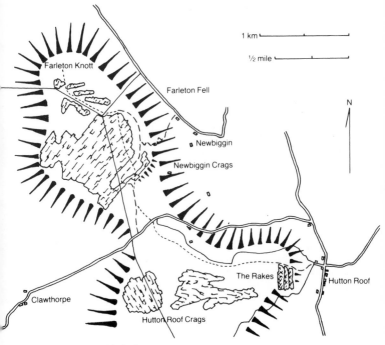

Hutton Roof and Newbiggin Crags

elsewhere in Britain, and account for Hutton Roof Crags being so widely known.

Return to the Blasterfoot Gap path, and then over the crest of the hill there is a choice of routes, none well defined. The easiest is along a sloping terrace on the north slope, while a rougher alternative crosses the chaos of broken pavements and low crags on the higher ground. The ways converge before crossing the road on to Farleton Fell – a broad sweep of green turf and white limestone lacking the trees and scrub of Hutton Roof. Through the gate, head straight across the pasture to the obvious white scars of Newbiggin

The Rakes on Hutton Roof

Crags. Here the limestone is horizontal but again has excellent pavements, the best of all being on a rock terrace halfway up the first scar. The joint-directed grykes form a square grid, and each clint block has a radial pattern of rounded karren grooves carved by over 10,000 years of rainwater since the ice retreated. The rock patterns created by the geometric fracture lines and the karren curves are beautiful: nature's handiwork at its best, and unique to limestone.

Continue northwards over Newbiggin Crags, and on the higher level the pavements continue. In parts, the clints and rounded karren grooves are like those of the lower terraces, but elsewhere the rock surfaces are broken and have a liberal cover of limestone chippings. The latter areas have been crudely quarried. The surface layer of a good limestone pavement consists of rounded clint blocks most of which are detached. Where the clints are small enough they are easily removed, without recourse to blasting, and so provide a cheap supply of stone; many blocks end up on rockeries and garden walls particularly of houses dating from the fifties and sixties. Unfortunately this working of pavements is very destructive to the landscape, and so is now heavily restricted. Newbiggin Crags, with its adjacent areas of worked and unworked pavements, show all too clearly the extent of damage to the limestone landforms – so slowly made but so quickly destroyed.

Continue over the pavements to the north, then descend a scar and join the track to the left, on to a footpath across more grassy pasture. It follows a natural break through scars edging sloping slabs of limestone and then rises to the cairns at the summit of Farleton Knott. The northern slopes are covered in screes and grass so it's hardly worth continuing, but there is a fine view ahead. Down below, the plain, now scored by the motorway, extends to the estuaries into Morecambe Bay. The peaks of the Lake District form the skyline far ahead and to the left, while over to the right a smoother profile is offered by the Howgill Fells and the Pennine summits. Before turning back, it is worth imagining standing on the same spot just 15,000 years ago – with the surface of the slowly-moving ice sheets some 500 m overhead. Daunting maybe, but that ice was responsible for so much of the landscape detail in the limestone country of today.

There is a public footpath over Hutton Roof, and accepted paths on the open pasture of Newbiggin Crags.

19 – Birkwith   802770

Ribblesdale widens out at its upper end, and with the railway and main road over on the west side, the eastern flanks below Birkwith Moor are left to the walkers. Access is easy with the road from Horton up to High Birkwith Farm, and cars may be left beside the track which extends beyond the farm to Old Ing. It is an ideal venue

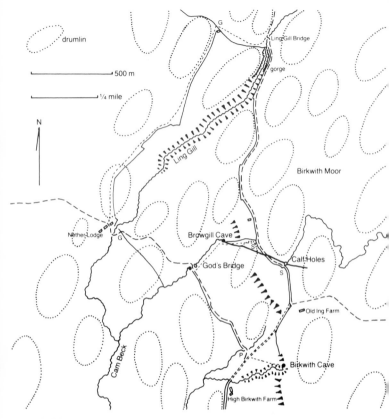

The Birkwith area

for the less energetic, as a circular walk can take in a number of caves and a fine gorge without the long climb normally needed to reach the limestone benches of the Three Peaks area.

A scatter of low scars and patches of white pavement are the unmistakable signs of limestone country, yet all around Birkwith

the landscape is dominated by rounded hills each about 300 m long
and 25 m high. These are drumlins, mounds of glacial boulder clay
smoothed and rounded by the ice which flowed over them 15,000
years ago. They are slightly enigmatic features, as nobody is quite
sure why the Ice Age glaciers chose to make and mould the
distinctive hills where they did; but, whatever the origin, the
drumlin field of Ribblesdale is Britain's finest. Between the
drumlins the boulder clay is so thin that streams draining down from
Birkwith Moor easily find the underlying limestone, and most
therefore sink into caves.

Continue up the track to Old Ing Farm, and through the gate turn
left, having joined the Pennine Way which has taken a high-level
route from Horton. By the next gate, a stile leads over the wall to
the right, to the lip of Calf Holes, also known as Dry Lathe Cave. A
good-sized stream flows between two drumlins and then cascades
into the open pothole, with a waterfall 10 m deep landing in a
shallow pool. A wire ladder may be on the shaft, indicating that
cavers are down below, but it is often hung down a small opening on
the left which drops into the roof of the downstream passage. It is a
popular cave as it provides a through trip to the Browgill
resurgence, but it is only negotiable by fully equipped cavers.

Return to the green track and follow it northwards, winding
between the drumlins until a deep valley opens up on the left. This
is Ling Gill, a splendid limestone ravine, which is now a National
Nature Reserve. The ravine is well wooded and the site is conserved
because it shows fine examples of the natural vegetation of the
limestone fells, protected from the ravages of sheep-grazing. There
is a stile by the Nature Conservancy sign into the reserve, but there
is no easy way down into the ravine. It is anyway desecration to
trample one of the few patches of surviving natural vegetation, so
stay on the green track outside the reserve – there are better views
further ahead too. The top end of the ravine narrows to a rocky
gorge which contains a fine example of massive block collapse. It
does not represent a collapsed cavern but is the result of progressive
undercutting where the stream water has found ways through joints
and beddings in its floor; this is the process which accounts for the
abundance of gorges where steep streams have eroded headwards

through limestone bedrock. In normal weather the stream sinks underground near the head of the gorge, but it emerges from the next bedding plane 10 m downstream, and then stays on the surface all the way down.

Ling Gill Bridge is a solid stone structure, a reminder of earlier centuries when it carried the monastic road over to Wensleydale, joining the Roman road across Cam Fell. Only the turnpike over Newby Head, built early in the last century and still the main road, saw its demise. Cross the bridge, then double back on a path over to New House Barn with its collapsed flagstone roof. Go through the gate to the left, then keep the walls on the left on the long stroll down to Nether Lodge. The ground may be rather wet, due to the boulder clay plastering the limestone, but there are fine views all around. The Three Peaks of, from left to right, Penyghent, Ingleborough and Whernside form the horizon; a round trip of all three makes a memorable day's walk for the energetic, though a time of two and a half hours is needed to win the annual Fell Race.

At Nether Lodge, keep left between the farm buildings then go over the bridge and up the track to a gate and stile. The rather rough green track was long ago designed to pass over God's Bridge. This is a common name in the Dales, always referring to a natural limestone bridge over a stream. Brow Gill Beck descends from the left to drop into the cave which has a roof 2 m thick for less than 15 m of length, but which is long enough to pass beneath the track. From the upstream end, daylight can be seen at the exit, but there is a deep pool in between, and the roof is too low for comfort.

Cross the bridge then follow up the south side of the beck, over a few low scars, to the entrance of Browgill Cave. The stream pours out of this classic resurgence cave at the end of its underground journey from the Calf Holes sink. The entrance is of walk-in size with only shallow water across its floor, and a walk to the limit of daylight gives a lovely view back out. Those with good torches can continue upstream walking on ribs of polished rock fretted by the stream. The passage is a 4 m high rift with bedding plane ledges on each side; but 50 m in, the stream has followed the bedding plan in a

Looking out of Browgill Cave

low wide passage. This acts as a natural barrier for the visitor; more than anything else, a helmet-mounted lamp is needed to leave both hands free to negotiate the crawl and a rift beyond which requires a degree of climbing agility. The equipped caver can continue up a by-pass round an underground waterfall and then into more low passages through to the streamway which extends to the foot of the shaft in Calf Holes.

From the Browgill entrance there is a choice of routes back to the Birkwith roadhead. Either go up above the cave to a stile on to the Pennine Way, or retrace steps to God's Bridge and then follow that track to the south. Just across the road, Birkwith Cave is worth a short diversion. It has a low wide bedding plane entrance out of which pours a powerful stream, returning to daylight the drainage from a line of sinkholes along the upper fellside. While the caves and gorges of the Birkwith area are of pocket size, they are all classic examples of their types, and for any walker who turns to the sport of caving Calf Holes may well be one of his first underground experiences.

There is a small fee for car parking at High Birkwith, but there is then free access to all the footpaths and caves; the Ling Gill Nature Reserve should not be entered without a Nature Conservancy permit.

20 – Thorns Gill   778799

Ribblehead is a broad area of low relief where Ice Age glaciers converged before diverging to flow south on either side of Ingleborough. It lies very close to the top of the limestone, so that its floor is dotted with caves and white scars, while the Yoredale rocks form higher ground on nearly all sides. The main drainage is Gayle Beck, which comes from the north and passes through Thorns Gill, before flowing away, rechristened the River Ribble. The gill is cut in limestone, a clean-washed little canyon where some of the water flows underground.

The old Gearstones Inn lies 2 km east of the famous railway

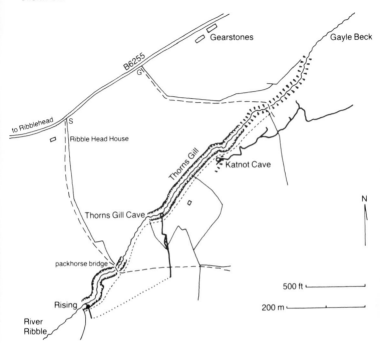

Thorns Gill and its caves

viaduct; a century ago it was the scene of important weekly markets but now it is a walkers' hostel. A little west of it, a gateway leaves the road and a footpath cuts down the fields to a footbridge at the top end of Thorns Gill. Upstream the view is of Gayle Beck flowing over slabs of limestone in a valley constrained between drumlins of grass-covered boulder clay. Downstream the beck has cut progressively deeper into the upper beds of the strong limestone, and Thorns Gill is a gorge 8 m deep and a little wider. Its walls are deeply undercut along some bedding planes, and the floor is a succession of deep, rounded pools. Downstream from the bridge, the path follows the left bank, giving views into the gill, and then drops down to a lower ledge just past a double bend.

In the back wall of the ledge, a hole 3 m high and wide is the entrance to Katnot Cave (sometimes called Capnut Cave). It is well worth a look inside for it has a fine stream passage easily explored with just wellingtons and a good torch. The entrance is dry but slopes down to a streambed where the water disappears under the right wall – and emerges from a spring a few metres down the gill. Upstream is a chamber 5 m high and 3 m wide, though there is also an impressively wide undercut bedding plane at floor level on either side of the central gravel bank. The stream is ponded by the gravel so that the upstream passage has about 25 m of pools which are no more than knee-deep but only traversable dry in wellingtons with a little care. Beyond them the floor rises where the stream cascades over low rock ledges, and the cave continues as a splendid, clean-washed, canyon passage a metre or more wide; the level bedding plane roof means that the height starts at 5 m but progressively descends. After 100 m or so the cave is a square-cut 2 m high and wide, the stream still flowing clear over gravel banks and through shallow pools cut in scalloped rock. Another 100 m on the roof lowers to force stooping then crawling, though it does still continue before closing down to a narrow bedding plane slot. Turn back before it becomes uncomfortable, and enjoy all the more this excellent example of a clean youthful stream cave.

Beyond Katnot, continue down the side of the gill. It opens out a little, but then drops back between vertical walls. Just past an old barn and a noisy waterfall barely a metre high, a tree pinpoints a scramble down to the streambed just before another double bend containing a deep pool. A few metres upstream of the tree, most of the beck turns into a hole in the rock wall of its left bank. This is Thorns Gill Cave, but do not be tempted to venture in; it cannot be followed far, the floor is a mass of slippery boulders, the roof is dark, low and dangerously uneven, and it floods with spectacular speed. It is an underground drainage loop which has captured the surface beck, and could one day leave the downstream gorge dry.

Return to the path and continue down beside a much-reduced stream flowing in a little gully cut in white limestone. An old

Thorns Gill Cave

packhorse bridge, beginning to suffer from age, spans the beck where it runs into a last section of miniature gorges with vertical walls dropping 5 m into deep pools. The last pool is the largest of all, and the main beck reappears from a tiny cave opening not easily picked out in its broken wall. Both path and gorge stop where a low scar marks the end of the strong limestone bed. Return to the old bridge, and take the path across it rising on to a drumlin from where there is a splendid panoramic view of the well-known Three Peaks and the two broad glaciated valleys which separate them. The path continues up to the road keeping right of a barn which is the very faded remnant of Ribble Head House.

Thorns Gill offers a short and very pleasant walk, best for relaxation on a warm summer day. It is however an excellent section of valley floor scenery in limestone country, with the fine streamway of Katnot Cave, the clean-washed gorge and the disappearing beck.

Public footpaths connect the road to both ends of the gill, and the farmer does not restrict reasonable use of the lower path over his land alongside the beck.

21 – Bruntscar Cave   738789

Beneath the dark slopes of Whernside, a thin line of farms commands magnificent views across the Ribblehead bowl: to the left, the famous railway viaduct so much a feature of the rolling fells, and to the right the steeper slopes of Ingleborough. Most of the farms stand against low limestone scars, as does Bruntscar Farm which is also almost on top of its own cave entrance. The approach to Bruntscar is along the tarred road from just below the Hill Inn, crossing the valley bottom where it is almost permanently dry; the farm is the first on the of the track where it parallels the scar.

A weathered sandstone slab, over the farm doorway, dates the building to 1689. It is still lived in, but the stone barn attached to the back of it is no longer in use. Doorways through the barn lead to the limestone scar against which it is built, and the cave entrance opens into the narrow gap between scar and barn. Reputation has it that the farm was built before the cave was discovered. Probably the entrance was originally obscured by fallen blocks, but the builders must have known there was something there as the water which issues from the scar is channelled beneath the farmhouse floor and also provided the original drinking supply. Perhaps later the entrance was enlarged, for it is now an easy walk-in.

Inside, the passage is a couple of metres high and wide with a stony floor, the little stream escaping under one wall just before it reaches daylight. It is a fairly clean canyon meandering gently, with a roof gently arched above the bedding plane which was originally found by the cave stream. Joints allow a slightly higher roof section and also guide seepage water which is depositing flowstone. There is then a section of passage with a beautiful tapered arch profile; it is arrow-straight along a single joint which is recognisable in both the polished floor and the narrow roof slot. Even though it is short, the joint passage is a perfect example of a limestone fracture enlarged by a cave stream.

Upstream another joint passage is not so well defined, is slightly curved, and unfortunately lowers, so that crawling is only just avoided, though the sound of falling water beckons from ahead. The cascade, little over a metre high, is easily overcome, and the passage above is tall but narrow enough to enforce a sideways shuffle in parts. There is no guiding joint here, for the passage twists and meanders freely beneath the bedding plane roof from which the stream started to cut its trench. Another waterfall in a little chamber has a deep pool at its foot and an even narrower passage above. This is the place for the casual visitor to turn back, for the continuing passage becomes progressively more constricted. Only a caver, prepared to crawl, squeeze and get wet, can follow the stream to a little chamber almost at its source where a hillside beck sinks into the limestone close to Hodge Hole Barn.

Perhaps the most unusual feature of Bruntscar Cave is the nature of its entrance. But for the wanderer through limestone country, it is worth a passing visit for the very attractive stream passage.

Permission to visit the cave is gained at the adjacent farm, where a church collection box welcomes donations.

22 – Hull Pot   808725

Horton in Ribblesdale is a straggling village on the floor of the dale directly between the hills of Penyghent and Ingleborough. Though as a farming community Horton dates back to a mention in the Domesday Book, a large part of its viability is now tourism and quarrying; notwithstanding the latter it is one of the main centres for walking in the limestone dales country. The best way out of the village is towards Penyghent, on a path which, even though it heads north-east, is the south-bound Pennine Way.

Horton Scar Lane is a surviving segment of an ancient packhorse

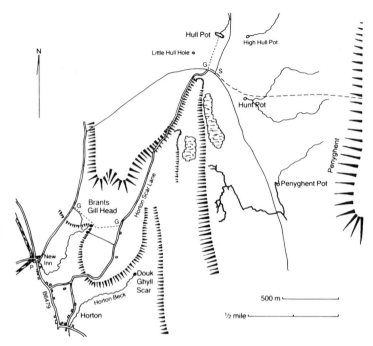

The Hull Pot area

road which used to go right over to Littondale. It leaves the main
road just south of the car park, and starts a steady rise. From just
beyond the last houses, Penyghent is visible straight ahead. It has a
distinctive stepped profile caused by the resistant bands of
limestone and sandstone within the Yoredale sequence of rocks
which form the summit mass above the main limestone platform.
Unfortunately the view behind, towards Ingleborough, is marred by
the Beecroft limestone quarry – a totally unnecessary eyesore in the
heart of the National Park. Down below the lane to the right, the
stream from Douk Ghyll Scar keeps out of sight; after a spell of wet

weather it can easily be heard, though in dry conditions its flow
stops completely – but more of that later.

The lane provides really easy walking, gaining height almost
unnoticeably. There are fine views across to Penyghent, and, down
below, a dry valley serves as a reminder of limestone's underground
drainage. Stronger beds in the limestone form low scars contouring
the hillside, and also a couple of steps in the valley floor. The lower
step is normally a 5 m high dry waterfall, but in wet weather a small
stream emerges at the top, cascades down the rock and sinks
underground again only a short distance below.

At the top of the limestone, the lane ends and a broad grassy
valley stretches ahead. Keep to the valley floor and it is impossible
to miss Hull Pot. The great square-cut hole almost looks as if it has
been quarried. It is 90 m long and nearly 20 m deep and wide; a
rocky streambed ends at its far lip, and down below the floor is of
boulders, cobbles and gravel. It lies on a fault where the broken
limestone has been easily eroded by the large stream draining from
the north. There has never been an underground cavern which has
collapsed, but the pothole has grown large due to the progressive
crumbling back of the walls – as can be seen by the huge slumped
blocks at the western end. In dry weather, no water enters Hull Pot.
Walk up the streambed for about 100 m, and the beck can be found
sinking into joints in the limestone. Between there and the pot
water can be heard in a few places cascading through the cave just
below the dry surface bed; and the stream can be seen emerging
into the east end of the pot before sinking in the boulder floor.

In wet weather, Hull Pot is seen at its best. The upstream sinks
are constricted and the stream flows over them until it cascades into
the open pothole. The 15 m high waterfall is a splendid sight.
Normally all the water sinks into the boulders, but the route
through them is also constricted and in really full flood, perhaps
only once a year, the pothole completely fills up, until it overflows
down the dry valley.

There is no easy way down into Hull Pot. A rift at the eastern end
needs a ladder, and a very exposed and dangerous climb at the
western end needs a lifeline. But the descent is hardly worth it – the
hole looks better from the top. Even cavers cannot go much further;

a side shaft reaches another 40 m down but even at that depth only leads back into the chaos of boulders beneath the main pothole floor.

For a complete contrast to Hull Pot, follow the Pennine Way towards Penyghent and just beside the path lies Hunt Pot. A small stream flows from the peat bogs, cascades down a staircase of ledges and then disappears into a vertical rift. It is easy to walk down past a few blocks to a safe stance at the northern end of the rift by a jammed boulder. The view down is eerie. The stream is broken over the lip so that it falls like a deluge of monsoon rain to dissolve into the darkness. No floor is visible, though in fact it lies 30 m down and is followed by yet another deep waterfall shaft. Hunt Pot is probably the classic pothole – a dramatic entrance to the underground.

Above Hunt Pot, the path continues for the energetic to the summit of Penyghent. Without the underground drainage of limestone, it has, under the ceaseless pounding of feet, become a wide muddy scar up the hillside; and anyway the better ascent of Penyghent is up the south end from Dale Head.

On the way back to Horton, make a detour to the west on a little-used path which passes by Brants Gill Head. This powerful spring is the resurgence for the waters sinking in Hull, Hunt and a host of other pots, for it lies very close to the base of the limestone. The path skirts above the stream head and from the west side the cave exit can be seen. It is hardly worth the descent to investigate, as the roof descends to the water only a few metres inside. A feature of Brants Gill is its very constant flow even in times of wet weather. This is because somewhere inside the unexplored cave system there is a constriction which controls a maximum flow to the spring. Excess water then takes another, overflow, route through the limestone and emerges at Douk Ghyll Scar, where again unfortunately there is no way in for cavers. Douk Ghyll is therefore often completely dry, but in wet weather produces huge volumes of water which flow down Horton Beck through the south end of the village.

The Brants Gill drainage system must have some unusual plumbing in its limestone caves, and it will remain an unexplored mystery for years to come. Hull Pot and Hunt Pot are just two of its inlet sinks, which, even though they cannot be followed far underground, are blessed with spectacular entrances.

All this route is on public footpaths.

23 – Penyghent Pot 829734

Lying not far south of Hunt Pot, Penyghent Pot has a remarkably uninspiring entrance in the shadow of the hill from which it takes its name. Close to a small stream sink, the entrance was dug through boulder clay in 1949, but it still gives no impression that beneath it lies the finest stream pothole in Britain. Penyghent Pot may be a magnificent feature of the geology and hydrology of limestone drainage, but it has achieved fame for the sporting delights which it offers through a perfect match of difficulty and rewarding spectacle.

Perhaps the most significant feature of a descent of Penyghent Pot is that the caver is almost never out of the water – it is the classic 'wet trip'. It starts with 300 m of crawling, partly flat-out, partly on hands and knees and all in water. Then there is a short wet ladder pitch, followed by the long Easy Passage – walking but with the roof low enough to make it back-breaking work with a load of ropes and ladders for waterfalls to come. These two passages seem to be there just to make the caver suffer before he reaches the spectacular caverns beyond.

For at the second waterfall the stream has broken away from the nearly level bedding planes of the limestone, and has found a major fracture system. The main shaft is 40 m deep, its floor lashed by the spray and wind from the cascading stream, and it is the top end of a splendid rift passage. Almost straight, along the line of the rock fracture, the stream rushes along dropping to lower depths at every opportunity. Showers of water rain from the roof at many places, for the fracture system is a real collector of the limestone drainage. Cascade follows cascade in this natural staircase, and through all the noise and the water it is an exciting descent for the caver.

The rift passage ends in a wide pool. Across the water, the way on is through Boulder Chamber, the only dry spot in the whole cave, and then back to the stream and down another cascade. Suddenly the atmosphere changes; there is another almost level section of cave with silent dark water moving through deep canals and low galleries. A side tunnel on the right brings in far more water than has come down the rift passage. This is the drainage from Hunt and Little Hull Pots, though a flooded section makes the connection

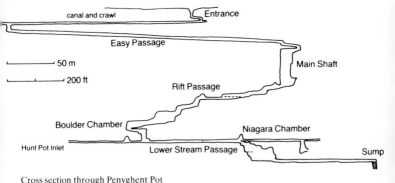

Cross section through Penyghent Pot

through impossible for cavers. In truth this is the main drain of the cave; the passage from the entrance is really only a tributary inlet, but happens to be the only one explorable from daylight.

The combined waters form a small underground river swirling through the wide galleries. The limestone walls are dark and sombre, the atmosphere is heavy; more than anything else, the lower passages of Penyghent Pot give a real feeling of depth. But ahead there is the noise of further cascades; the water hurtles over a trio of falls in the aptly-named Niagara Chamber. It creates a cacophony of wind, spray and noise, and is almost the final climax of this magnificent cave. Another few hundred metres of tunnel, almost level, with the water flowing swiftly, then down a last short step into a deep black sump pool. Its level is the same as the pool in Brants Gill Head, and the final stage of this underground river is unfollowable as it loops deeply down through totally and permanently flooded passages. The water finds its way through but the caver has to return up the long series of cascades, rifts and canals to the single entrance high on the hillside.

Penyghent Pot is unforgettable. It is not the deepest, nor the longest cave in the country. But its powerful streams and rivers, carved into the raw limestone, are the epitome of an active cave system. Almost inconceivable from the surrounds of green grass and

The main drain in Penyghent Pot

blue skies, it is a vital component of the limestone landscape. Even though a descent of Penyghent Pot is arduous and tiring, perhaps cavers are the lucky ones for having the chance to see this hidden half of the natural world.

Permission to descend Penyghent Pot is obtained through the Council of Northern Caving Clubs.

24 – Hammer Pot   853697

There is nothing at Hammer Pot to appeal to either the passing walker or about 90 per cent of all cavers. Its entrance is an insignificant little hole on the rather bleak western slopes of Fountains Fell. Inside, its passages are so narrow that most cavers have no hope of ever exploring them. But therein lies the reason for the inclusion of Hammer Pot in this review of the Pennine limestone country.

When it was first explored, by local cavers in 1957, progress was only possible through the narrow entrance passages after tiny flakes had been brayed off the walls with a lump hammer. Hence the name given to the cave. Even with the flakes removed, the cave was still extremely tight, and more hammering was needed along further passages. Eventually the explorers were rewarded when they reached larger and very spectacular caverns beyond, and the whole epic constituted a major step forward in terms of the difficulty of caves and the determination with which cavers would attack any obstacle. Since 1957 even tighter underground passages have been explored elsewhere in the Yorkshire Dales, but none has led through to such fine stream caves beyond. It is this aspect which makes Hammer Pot alone such a classic. A trip through the narrow sections and into the river passage beyond is much more than just a demonstration of masochism; it is, though some may find it hard to believe, a superb experience, and a genuine achievement.

Straight in from daylight, Hammer Pot is a narrow little stream canyon less than a metre high. The water is no problem, but the repeated tight bends require endless contortions to get the length of the body round them. Known as the First Narrows, where the hammer was used on the original explorations, it is not now too serious a problem, and soon ends with a wider passage to a short ladder pitch into a chamber. The Second Narrows leads straight off from the chamber, and is a truly remarkable passage. It is a stream canyon with plenty of height – 5 m or more. Over thousands of years the tiny stream has carved away at its floor with amazing uniformity. Walls of scalloped limestone are almost parallel, and nowhere more than 25 cm apart. Once the caver enters the Narrows he cannot turn his head or his feet; walking, or rather squeezing, along crabwise he has to carry ladders and ropes for the shafts beyond and every few metres has a sharp bend to negotiate. The twisting rift is only about 70 m long, but for over half its length there is no usable floor. The stream is in an even tinier slot below, and it is all too easy to slip down and become jammed. The explorers dropped wooden blocks into the tapering rift; these stemples help but they are far apart. It's a continuous struggle; and then the rift narrows even more. The way on is to slide down into a wider section below; gravity helps on the way in but it is an awful thrutch on the way out. A climb into a chamber and the tight section is finished; the way ahead is open.

A pleasant stream canyon continues, wide enough for easy walking. Two shafts provide refreshing showerbaths on the ladder climbs. Then Hammer Pot replies with its second *pièce de résistance*. The roof drops sharply to only half a metre above the floor; the stream slithers away over liquid mud. Sludge Crawl, aptly named, is 100 m long. The caver wallows along trying not to make waves, his head on one side to keep his face out of the brown sludge. The cave roof becomes progressively lower, till his face is half in the water and mire – one eye, one nostril and a gasping mouth almost scraping the roof. Ahead, a rumbling noise grows ever lower, and round a corner Sludge Crawl pops out into the river passage.

A torrent sweeps by from left to right; downstream is larger and beckons the explorer forward. It is an exciting passage, with plenty of space and bouncing, noisy water. Deep potholes break the rock floor and it is still no place to rush, yet the river pours relentlessly on. The gradient steepens with more white water, before a little cascade, and then a 15 m shaft where the torrent falls into oblivion. A ladder can be hung clear of the waterfall, but down below the splendour is short-lived. Through low crawl passages past wide shingle banks, the water shortly flows into a deep black pool, a sump beyond which the permanently flooded passages are unexplored.

Though its appeal may be only to the very energetic sporting caver, Hammer Pot is still one of the finest caves in Britain. As unattainable for most people as is the summit of Mount Everest, its lower reaches remain an extremely remote place right in the heart of England – a paradox perhaps but a very real part of our limestone landscape.

Permission to descend Hammer Pot is obtained through the Council of Northern Caving Clubs.

25 – Victoria Cave   836631

The limestone hills just east of Settle are only briefly glimpsed from either the town or the Malham road. Away from the roads, some impressive panoramas are unfurled from footpaths which provide pleasant walking on easy gradients. The lines of white crags and scars are broken by a number of cave entrances, of which the largest and most famous is Victoria Cave. It is nearest to the Langcliffe road to the north, but is best approached by the slightly longer walk from the south, or on one of a choice of circular routes.

Cars can be left on the Settle to Malham road close to where the lane turns off to Stockdale Farm. At the second corner on the lane, the footpath is signposted to Attermire Scar and cuts up a grassy slope past an old lime kiln. Beyond the isolated knoll of Sugar Loaf Hill, the ground falls away and there is a splendid view along a whole line of limestone crags, from Warrendale Knotts on the left to Attermire Scar on the right. This impressive line has been eroded from the edge created by the Middle Craven Fault which extends east-west just in front of the scars. The fault has displaced the limestone to the south downwards by about 100 m, and the main crags are about that height too, broken into separate buttresses by minor north–south faults. The whole area was overrun by Ice Age glaciers which moved from the north and helped to pluck clean the south-facing scars.

Follow the marked path through gates and stiles to the foot of the scars, and then take the line which heads obliquely up the grassed screes towards the centre of Attermire Scar. Down to the right, the dark reed grasses mark the flat wet ground which was drained only a century ago; before that it was the shallow lake, or mire, which gave the overlooking scar its name. In the middle of the scar, a dark vertical rift is the entrance to Attermire Cave. The path turns straight up the scree towards it, then goes left on to a grassy ledge which cuts back to the cave 5 m up the sheer rock wall. Only about 3 m high and 2 m wide, the entrance leads to a muddy rift which can be followed for 50 m before it becomes rather low, though it is hardly worth the effort of carrying a torch. A wealth of Romano–British material, including the metalwork of a native

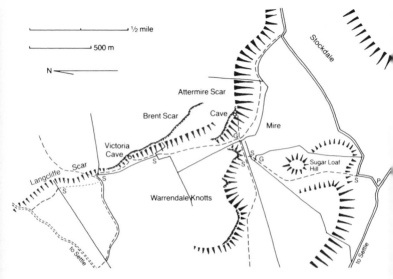

Victoria Cave and Attermire Scar

chariot, has been dug from the cave sediment, and it would appear
that the cave was then sacred – a votive site associated with death
ceremonies; the entrance was hardly large enough to have provided
a reasonable living shelter.

  Below the ledge from the cave entrance, a path contours round
the top of the screes to the west and turns into the valley running
north. It continues beneath the crags of Brent Scar and then the
southern end of the long Langcliffe Scar, with views ahead to a
distant Ingleborough. The path is driven towards the scars by a wall,
but then cuts up the scree directly to Victoria Cave. A broad flat
terrace stands in front of the cave entrance, whose yawning mouth is
12 m high and wide. The single chamber extends in about 40 m, its
roof stepped on different bedding planes and broken by a few
solutional rifts. Its floor is a sloping mass of boulders and dry mud,
with some stone-covered polythene sheeting over some of the lower

Victoria Cave breaks the line of Langcliffe Scar

undisturbed clay. Side galleries on the left barely extend out of
daylight and are rather muddy.

Victoria Cave is well known for the fossil and archaeological
material which its sediment yielded mainly during massive
excavations in the last century. Stand back on the terrace outside,
look at the entrance and think that 150 years ago it was completely
blocked by sediment. The only way in then was the little entrance
higher up to the left, and this led into a low cave where the mud
floor met the roof over much of the area now occupied by the main
chamber. All that excavated sediment now forms the terrace in
front of the entrance. The digging did yield much bone material.
The lower layers had bones of hippo and rhino, which have now
been dated, by the uranium contents of encrusting stalagmite, to
120,000 years ago – putting them in the warm period of the last

interglacial when those animals temporarily roamed the Dales. Pottery fragments in the upper layers indicate Stone Age man's presence in the cave, but then the top layers and the original floor yielded large amounts of bone and metal material from the Romano–British period of just 2000 years ago. Like Attermire, it would seem that Victoria Cave too was a votive site and most of the material was placed or thrown there as ceremonial offerings.

Before returning to the south, walk at least as far as the brow of the hill, where there is a fine view north. Beyond the broken scars of Winskill and Langcliffe, the glacial trough of Ribblesdale, scarred by its stone quarries, extends into the distance with Moughton Scar and Ingleborough rising on its left. A path does continue over stiles as far as the Langcliffe road, and others loop round to Settle or go up past the low entrances of the short Jubilee Cave on to the open moor. Otherwise, return past Victorian Cave, and perhaps consider the times millennia ago when the hippos wandered in and out of the entrance, then wide open, and in a splendid setting of the very best limestone country.

The walk is all on public and concession paths, with open access to the caves.

26 – Malham Cove   90027

Malham is one of the main tourist centres of the Yorkshire Dales, and rightly so, because it is an attractive village with a splendid setting backed by Malham Cove – perhaps the best-known landscape feature in the area. For most visitors, the walk to the Cove is through the village from the large car park by the Park information centre.

The origins of Malham can be traced back 1300 years to a settlement centred on the present green. Four centuries later the village was cut in two when the beck formed the boundary of lands owned by Fountains Abbey and Bolton Priory. But the dissolution of the monasteries saw new prosperity; most of the old wooden houses were replaced by the stone buildings which form the core of the village today, and in 1636 the beck was crossed by the humped packhorse bridge – which survives today, though widened and graded. Keep west of the beck through the upper village, and the last building on the left is Calamine House. It takes its name from the zinc mineral mined early in the last century from veins on Pikedaw Hill and stored here before shipment to the Midlands brass foundries.

Just beyond the houses a path leaves the road to the right heading straight for the Cove, and the first view is impressive. Vertical white cliffs of massive limestone cut an arc through the grass slopes. Various figures are quoted for the height of Malham Cove, but it is exactly 70 m in the centre where the crest is nicked by a small dry valley; on each side the cliffs rise another 10 m where grassed screes mask the base. The total width is 200 m, and grassed ledges extend in from both ends but do not reach the blank central wall. It is a monumental scar and, though it is featured in nearly everyone's school geography lessons, its origin is still open to debate. At least in part it is a dry waterfall, cut long ago when a river flowed overground and not underground, and retreated from the edge of the limestone hills marked by the Middle Craven Fault just north of Malham village. Undercutting by spring sapping and cave erosion may have helped ensure the verticality of the cliffs. But both the valley above and the cave below are so small that these can only have been contributory factors and it is likely that most of the rock removed from the foot of the Cove was scoured away by Ice Age glaciers.

The path to the foot of the Cove is a pedestrian highway, but along its route look out for signs of the farming history. The dry-stone walls across the valley date back to the Enclosure Acts of about 200 years ago. Above the beck to the right, horizontal terraces in the fields are the lynchets built to improve the land about 1000 years ago. Even older are the low grass ridges, again across the valley floor, which are all that remain of Celtic field boundaries from about 2000 years ago. They are not easily seen from ground level, but the evening sun picks them out well in a view from the top of the Cove.

Through a thin stand of trees, the path ends abruptly at the foot of the Cove. Vertically overhead the 70 m of limestone is either a white sunlit wall or perhaps an overhanging shadow disappearing into low cloud; either way it is very impressive. The beck issues from a small pool at the foot of the cliff, and behind the surface rubble cave-divers have found a bedding plane passage just below water level; unfortunately it is too low after 150 m and the caves behind remain a mystery.

The direct route to the top of the Cove requires energetic and acrobatic climbing, with a fair proportion of artificial techniques on some of the holdless walls. Most Sundays see a number of climbers on the Cove, but they tend to be on the eastern flank where the limestone, though not so high, offers better-quality routes. For the walker the path is up the west side, where its popularity has required the National Park to build a long flight of steps so as to avoid the serious erosion on random trails all over the hillside. But for those going to both top and bottom of the Cove the best way to see it for the first time is from the top.

The shortest approach is from the road to the west. The two spectacular roads across the limestone fells, from either Arncliffe or Langcliffe, join west of Malham Tarn and then lead south. Cars can be left on the wide verge just before the sign banning any parking for the rest of the way down to the village. Over the stile to the left, head straight across the alternating grass and pavements, and down a gentle slope to the rim of the scars above the Watlowes. This is a classically beautiful dry valley with lines of white limestone crags overlooking a level grass floor. A number of thin paths drop through the scars, and it is then a superb walk down the Watlowes to the lip of Malham Cove. The last few metres are over limestone pavement and only the distant views indicate the presence of the cliff, but it is possible to get right to the edge for an aerial view of the ant-sized people by the beck 80 m below. Across to the right, the clint blocks of the pavement have been polished by countless feet, and a triple stile stands at the top of the path down to the foot of the Cove and the village. But stay above the wall and head up the slope, to where high stiles over more walls mark the path back to the road and the parking place.

Best of all the walks, however, is the long loop from Malham, up

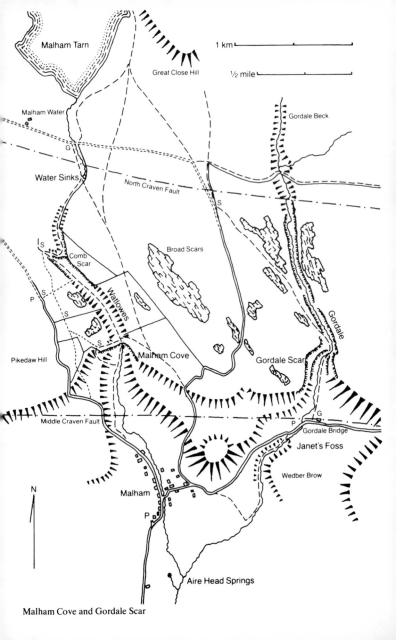

Malham Cove and Gordale Scar

Malham Cove

through Gordale, past the Tarn, and then down the Watlowes, to pass the Cove. This can take the best part of a day and is one of Britain's classic geography field trip walks. The Gordale route is described below, so continue to the Tarn to pick up the whole story of the cove. Malham Tarn is a natural lake sitting on a bed of impermeable slates – though its northern shore laps against the saturated zone of the overlying limestone. A small earth dam does stabilise the level of the lake – it was built in 1791 along with the sluice gates to control the outflow. Malham Water flows south, under the road, and then across the North Craven Fault – which brings limestone to its bed instead of slate. Consequently the water sinks just a little way downstream; unfortunately the sink is into streambed debris and there is no open cave.

It would seem logical that this would be the water which re-emerges at the foot of the cove, but this is not the case. Back in the 1870s the tarn sluices were used to send a short flood pulse down into the sink. Careful monitoring of stream levels then showed that the flood pulse did not reappear at the Cove, but at Aire Head Springs, 700 m south of Malham village. Furthermore, ammonium sulphate was placed in a sink near an old smelt mill chimney, a kilometre to the west, and this was recorded at the Cove Rising. Malham therefore became famous as one of the earliest places where it was demonstrated that underground streams could cross over independently of each other within the complex drainage systems of limestone caves. 100 years later the tests were repeated, using more sophisticated techniques with fluorescent dyes, and showed that though the main story holds true there is also some flow which goes from both sinks to both springs. Limestone hydrology is certainly complex.

Beyond the water sinks, follow the path down into the deepening dry valley. Limestone scars on each side become higher, a short cave breaks the left wall, and then the path curves to the right. This is to avoid the dry waterfall of Comb Scar, and it doubles round to cross a stile into a tributary gully. Just down into the gully, look at the rock on the left wall which is a superb example of fault breccia with broken limestone fragments in a matrix of calcite. The fault and the gully give easy access to the floor of the Watlowes and the splendid walk down to the top of the Cove. Though the Watlowes is now dry, it carried a powerful meltwater river about 14,000 years ago. This was as the Ice Age glaciers melted away, yet the still-frozen limestone did not allow the water underground – and this was when most of the valley erosion took place, before the drainage found its way back into the caves. Powerful though the Watlowes river must have been, it seems overshadowed by the erosive forces that cut Malham Cove, still an anomalously large landscape feature.

The scenery around Malham Cove is nothing short of spectacular. It deserves its popularity purely on that score, but in addition the area is a textbook piece of limestone country whose geology and hydrology hide a fascinating story and still a few unsolved problems.

The routes are all on public and concession footpaths.

27 – Gordale Scar   914635

Malham is one of the most popular centres in the Yorkshire Dales because of its spectacular limestone scenery which culminates in the twin features of the Cove and Gordale Scar. Though both sites are dominated by particularly high limestone cliffs, cut by erosion into the plateau edge defined by the Middle Craven Fault, they are very different in character. The wide open, white cliff of Malham Cove contrasts with the shadows closed in between the towering crags of Gordale Scar.

Access is easy on the little road which goes east from Malham village to Gordale Bridge, across the beck from the Scar, where there is room to park cars. Before heading for the tall cliffs, turn back down the road a short way to where the beckside footpath leads down to Janet's Foss. A wide round plunge pool catches a waterfall which drops 5 m into it, with trees framing a most attractive spot. The foss, or the waterfall, is a smooth chute of water pouring over a bank of tufa some 4 m wide. Tufa is rather like stalagmite in that it is calcium carbonate precipitated from lime-saturated water, but it is formed in a surface stream where algae grow and cause the precipitation by altering the water chemistry. Along Gordale Beck the tufa is on an unusually large scale, some being inactive, but some, as here, still forming. At Janet's Foss it has grown out over a rock ledge to create a small cave almost behind the waterfall, and the name comes from the legendary fairy queen who once lived there; the cave, easily reached by a scramble on the far side of the fall, is however a rather unwelcoming place to live.

Above Gordale Bridge the beck cuts across a wide floor of gravel with a cover of rich grass, and a good path follows the eastern bank. The fault line is soon crossed where the limestone crags rise sharply

Gordale Scar

on both sides, and the cliffs ahead narrow towards the Scar. It is a dramatic approach in a splendid rock landscape, but the immensity of the gorge is only appreciated on rounding a sharp corner to the right. In this inner section of Gordale Scar, vertical and overhanging rock walls rise 50 m on each side; at their narrowest they are only 15 m apart. They rise unbroken and straight from the stony riverbed while more crags and scars rise above to the plateau surface over 100 m above the beck. Ahead the water cascades over a bank of tufa 10 m high, and there is an easy scramble up in the centre and clear of the water. Deep footholds and handholds have been carved into the spectacularly banded tufa, which at this point is inactive and is now being eroded by the beck.

Only a few metres ahead another waterfall pours from a hole punched right through a thin rib of towering limestone. The water drops 10 m into a natural amphitheatre, where the side walls are 50 m high, before running out over the lower tufa falls. The eyehole waterfall is actively depositing tufa on an algae-covered bank beneath it, and just to the left there is an even larger bank of old, dead tufa marking the site of an earlier waterfall. This was active until 1730 when the beck suddenly found its new route through the eyehole. The walls of the amphitheatre are cut by vertical notches along the lines of small faults, and one of these provides a convenient route out up to the left; it is rough scree at first but a new flight of steps makes the going easier and safer towards the top. The rock rib right of the steps can be crossed by a few routes which require a little scrambling and great care on some narrow ledges, and a path then drops to the beck above the eyehole – which frames an unusual view back down the gorge.

There is no footpath further upstream in Gordale, so follow the signs on a route which rises again to the left. From the top of the first scar there is a fine view both upstream into the valley, and downstream into the jaws of the gorge. The precise origin and age of Gordale are still debated, but there is little doubt that it was cut by meltwater flowing from retreating Ice Age glaciers. The upstream valley is a typical meltwater channel with rocky walls and today only a much reduced stream, and the depth of the main gorge can be credited to the enhanced erosive power of the water as it steepened its descent off the edge of the limestone plateau. The gorge of Gordale Scar is so narrow because all the energies of the stream went to deepening its bed and not widening its channel. Its downcutting may have been assisted by the unroofing of bits of cave within the limestone – such as the eyehole which survives today – but the popular idea of the gorge being a collapsed cavern really has no foundation or credibility.

From that lofty viewpoint, steps can be retraced down the gorge by those who don't wish for a longer walk. But the best walk of all in the Malham area is the round trip of Gordale, Watlowes and Malham Cove. So follow the path over the stile and across the grass between the patches of pavement which spread over the plateau. The route is well marked and meets the road near the line of the North Craven Fault. This marks the end of the limestone pavements, for the rock ahead is the slate which supports Malham Tarn, and the overlying limestone is only seen again on the higher scars such as Great Close Hill beside and beyond the Tarn. Loop round by the Tarn, or take the road across to Malham Water and there pick up the walk down the Watlowes dry valley to the Cove.

With or without the extended circular walk, Gordale Scar remains one of the most spectacular landforms in the Pennines. Its towering cliffs and brooding shadows are on a monumental scale. With the tops in cloud on a stormy day it is awe-inspiring, while a warm afternoon sun creates an exceptionally massive panorama of white limestone.

All the route is on public footpaths.

28 – Scoska Cave   930719

Littondale is a magnificent valley. Almost straight for 12 km, it has a cross-section rounded on a bold scale; instantly recognisable as a glaciated trough it owes its origin to a powerful stream of ice moving south-east away from the Dales ice centre of Pleistocene times. Ice-trimmed crags of white and grey limestone fringe much of the valley; they culminate at Arnberg Scar, just south of Arncliffe, a truncated spur only marginally less impressive than its down-valley neighbour at Kilnsey.

The level of activity shown by Ice Age erosion has hardly been matched in modern times. Littondale was a hunting forest owned by Fountains Abbey, and since the dissolution of the monasteries has been little more than a farming area. The eighteenth-century lead-mining boom almost completely passed it by, and the heights of industrial activity at Arncliffe were the corn mill and cotton mill, both now more than a century into the past. Arncliffe is an outstandingly attractive village with its stone-built houses around the broad green, and the church of St Oswald beautifully sited beside the river. But the village has retained its charm, never pulling in the tourist crowds even though it has achieved some fame through its television appearances in various Dales programmes.

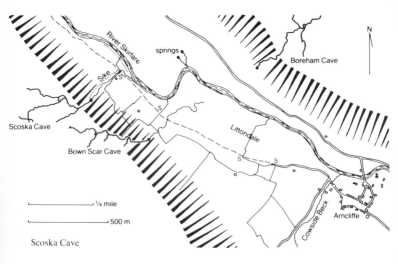

Scoska Cave

   The limestone of Littondale does contain its share of caves, which
are unusual in that all the major systems are entered only from the
lower end. The sinkholes and potholes along the high limestone
benches have no large or spectacular entrances, and none can be
followed to significant depths. Boreham Cave, just north of
Arncliffe, is best known for its beautifully decorated passages, but is
only accessible to divers who can pass the long entrance sumps.
Almost opposite it, on the western flank of Littondale, is Scoska
Cave which has a spacious 'walk-in' entrance.
   At the western end of the Arncliffe, just over the Cowside Beck
bridge, there is room to leave cars on the verge, beside the junction
with a walled track which is the signed footpath up the dale. In wet
weather the track doubles as a streambed, and wellingtons make the
walking easier. Across to the left there is a good view into the
Cowside valley, with its distinctive asymmetrical profile. The
limestone crags of Yew Cogar Scar on the south side contrast with
the grassy slopes of boulder clay which the road climbs on its north
side; this was caused by the edge of the Littondale glacier moving

across the valley, dumping sediment on the lee slope but then scouring the southern slope as it forced its way round and over it.

The path continues over a stile and across open meadows where the grandeur of Littondale can be really appreciated. Bown Scar Wood clads the scars on the left, and in wet weather a cascade of white water can be seen descending from its far end. This is the main drainage from the moors above emerging through Bown Scar Cave. Inside the cave, nearly all the passages are low crawlways following bedding planes in the limestone, and the entrance is comparably small – it does not merit a visit and anyway there is no path to it.

Stepping-stones, which have seen better days, take the path across Bown Scar Beck, beyond which the River Skirfare lies behind the levee on the right. In dry weather the channel is inactive as the whole river emerges from springs just across the dale having gone underground above Litton village. But the wet-weather flow has necessitated the building of the levee, and its stone dyke reinforcement, to prevent inundation of the floodplain meadows extending down to Arncliffe.

The entrance of Scoska Cave can be seen from the levee, a gaping black hole high in the woods. To reach it, cross the stile and the tiny stream of Guildersbank Sike, and then go up the grassy slope following a path into the woods. Water emerges from the hillside at many points in wet weather, but there is only ever a very small flow from the cave. Frost-shattering of the roof and walls has flared the cave entrance out to the scar, but inside it continues as a level gallery 2 m high and 4 m wide. It invites attention, and for family visitors is one of the few caves where it is safe to let children explore ahead a little way. The square-cut passage has a flat bedding plane roof, and a floor of broken slabs and sediment. The stream which formed it now emerges from Bown Scar; only a little percolation water now finds the passage and is depositing stalagmite along part of the floor.

A junction appears after 70 m of almost straight passage. The water emerges from the left branch, where a low crawl discourages visitors; the roof does rise further in and the passage continues for another 200 m. Ponder then the human bones 1500 years old found

Looking out of Scoska Cave

at its far end by the first modern cave explorers in 1905. More inviting is the right branch which continues at walking height though much narrower than the entrance gallery. It has the same bedding plane roof, but the floor of sediment gradually rises. A side passage at roof level on the right also follows the bedding plane but is only 30 cm high – it gives some idea of how the caves started to form before the stream cut the canyon in the floor. The floor continues to rise, and children find progress easier than adults, but after another 100 m the passage has become a straightforward crawl. It is best to turn back, for the remaining kilometre of cave further into the hill is practically all of only crawling height.

Even though the walking-size passages of Scoska are not long, the entrance gallery is unusually fine and the cave is well worth the visit.

It also provides an opportunity to see a little more of Littondale, surely one of the finest of the Pennine dales.

There is a public right of way along the valley floor, and a footpath in common use up to the cave, the landowner being at East Garth Farm in Litton.

29 – Strans Gill Pot   916788

Stalactites and stalagmites adorn almost every cave to some extent, and their infinite variety combines in an endless range of underground spectaculars. There will always be debate over which is the best-decorated cave passage in the Pennines, but a strong contender is the Passage of Time hidden in the depths of Strans Gill Pot. Fortunately, from the point of view of its conservation, the Passage of Time is way beyond the reach of the casual visitor, and the difficulties of Strans Gill Pot even keep many experienced cavers away. This may be a disappointment to the dedicated tourist, but it does mean that the Passage of Time will remain, known to many but seen by few, a very special corner of the Yorkshire Dales.

Tucked away on the limestone fell above Hubberholme, the entrance to Strans Gill Pot is little more than a fissure in the bedrock of the gill. It was covered by stream sediment and totally unknown until 1967 when two local cavers found it while out searching for new caves. Smooth dark rock, absolutely immovable, forms the walls of the fissure, which drops vertically for 12 m; in its upper section it is only 19 cm wide. This is just the first of the Strans Gill obstacles, and is completely impassable for most people. From the foot of the shaft there are just a few metres of narrow horizontal fissure leading directly to another short drop. It causes no problems on the way down, but getting off the top of the ladder on the way back up is extremely difficult. As if that were not enough, the next fissure is the most difficult of all the entrance squeezes – it tapers downwards and a caver spends a lot of effort to ensure that he does not slip down and wedge in the jaws of the rift.

Once beyond those narrow entrance rifts, Strans Gill Pot begins

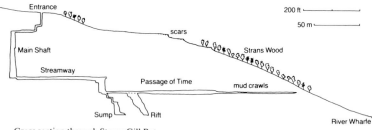

Cross section through Strans Gill Pot

to open up. The third squeeze leads on to a ledge overlooking a
magnificent 50 m deep shaft which offers a fine ladder or rope climb
down its centre. From below, a small stream passage continues to
the head of a very wet descent down a waterfall into a chamber.
Purely in terms of distance, this chamber is not far from the
entrance, but measured in time and effort the journey is a minor
epic. The reward is just around the corner. The stream drops into a
series of rifts which soon reach a sump, but a side passage leads
away into a zone of silence. It starts as a low crawlway, and develops
into a deep rift where a traverse over the top enlarges into the
Passage of Time.

Dark mudbanks create a sombre air as the tunnel curves away, no
more than 3 m high and twice as wide. Delicate, white straw
stalactites hang from the roof, and further down the passage they are
longer and more closely packed. Just round a gentle bend they
culminate in an incredible display. Many of the fragile straws are
over 2 m long, and they sparkle against the background of dark mud
and rock. There are some more massive stalactites, and even a few
joined to the floor in solid pillars. Flowstone covers some of the
mud banks, and rimstone pools cover the centre of the floor. There
is something indescribable about the Passage of Time; other caves
may have more calcite deposits, but few if any can match the perfect
balance of the formations which make this particular cave almost
like a work of art.

To the passing walker or motorist, Langstrothdale is a lovely
valley, but there is little sign of what lies beneath the limestone fells.

The surface is only half the story in limestone country, and Strans Gill Pot is one of the more beautiful components of the other half.

Permission to descend Strans Gill Pot should be obtained from the landowner at Yockenthwaite Farm.

The Passage of Time in Strans Gill Pot

30 – Dow Cave   984744

Lying in the deepest part of Wharfedale, Kettlewell is a village
which dates back 1000 years through a history of farming, mining
and marketing. Today it is more of a holiday centre for it has a
splendid setting and is surrounded by good walking country.
Limestone scars line both sides of Wharfedale, and indicate the
presence of cave systems deep beneath the fellsides. The finest of
these is Dow Cave, popular and well-known among experienced
cavers, but also with much to offer the visitor who does not object to
wet feet.

Take the Leyburn road which climbs steeply out of Kettlewell
and levels out along the floor of the Cam Gill valley. The road then
climbs the very steep hill of Park Rash, but there is room to park
cars on the shoulder by a small farm building at the foot. Walk up
the road 50 m to a stile over the right wall – on to the path which
leads directly to the cave. It is a pleasant ten-minute stroll along this
little valley to a footbridge which takes the path across to natural
limestone steps up into Caseker Gill. 100 m ahead a waterfall
tumbles over a limestone scar, but much more water emerges from a
pile of boulders on the right. The path crosses the beck, on rounded
water-worn slabs which are incredibly slippery, and then climbs the
boulder slope. And there lies the entrance of Dow Cave – a
handsome tunnel 8 m high and 3 m wide.

A good torch and reasonable boots or wellingtons are enough to
explore the main passage of Dow. Some of the pools are knee-deep;
they can be avoided by climbing on ledges but this is not
recommended, particularly when one hand is occupied with a torch;
it is much more enjoyable to get wet feet and avoid the antics –
appreciate the cave, and have some spare clothes in the car. Climb
down the boulders inside the cave, taking care with unadjusted eyes
in the deepening shadows. Ignore the ledges and descend to the
stream which loses itself into the boulders only to reappear outside;
normally the water is shallow but in very wet weather it can become
an impassable torrent. It flows in a trench a metre or so wide cut
into the floor of the massive canyon passage, and upstream
positively invites exploration.

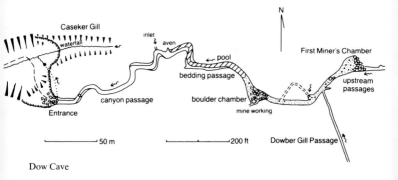

Dow Cave

   Follow the water, wading through the pools, only using the ledge
on the right to pass a couple of fallen blocks. The walls are ledged
well up into the roof, and high above there are some spectacular
jammed blocks – perfectly safe as they are well out of reach. The
canyon continues, and upstream its walls are cleaner though the
floor of cobbles rises steadily. Round a pair of fine wide meanders
the water still tumbles over rocks and by now the roof is only 5 m
above as it follows the same level bedding plane through the
limestone. Where an inlet splashes down on the left the canyon dies;
the floor steps up over a rock rib, a dripping aven breaks the roof
and then the passage is a wide bedding plane – it is 6 m across
through the roof is only 2 m high. A wide ledge traverses a deep
pool filling a floor trench, and passes into a zone of silence
contrasting with the noisy water of the downstream canyon.
   The pool continues with broad ledges overlooking the slow black
water from the right, and where the ledges are missing the water is
shallow with a sandy bottom. It is a magnificent passage and further
on the flat bedding roof, broken by just a few stalactites, spans a full
8 m. The pool ends and boulders rise into a small chamber. Ignore
the low stream route on the left and also the old mine workings on
the right; the Wharfedale lead-miners once used the natural cave
for access to the mineral veins deep inside the hill. Keep ahead
towards the sound of falling water, and past the tiny roof inlet

Ledges traverse the long pool in Dow Cave

continue up the boulders towards the obvious high-level hole; then walk down the slope into the large stream passage beyond. The walls are more broken in this upstream stretch, the roof steps up and down, and there are fallen blocks with the water often flowing beneath them. A stooping 'gorilla-walk' is needed for a section where the roof drops to little over a metre, but this soon ends where the roof rises beyond reach. A muddy side-passage goes round the low section, but it is even worse with a miserable grovel and a climb, so avoid it.

A narrow arched tube descending to the right is the ignominious start to one of the most remarkable cave passages in Britain. Dowbergill Passage continues almost dead straight for 1500 metres, following a single main joint in the limestone. It carries a small stream right through this shoulder of Great Whernside from the next valley to the south, almost due east of Kettlewell. There is another entrance near the sink, known as Providence Pot, and the traverse from Providence to Dow is one of the classic caving routes of the north. Unfortunately the straight rift passage is immensely complicated by boulder piles, lakes, narrows and wide sections all at different levels, so that route-finding in the vertical obstacle course is very difficult. The past has seen a number of inexperienced groups lost in Dowbergill Passage and needing rescue; and that is why the telephone wire is now a fixture in the roof of Dow Cave from the entrance to the junction.

Dowbergill is clearly not for the casual visitor, so continue past it, clamber over the large boulders, and follow the last few metres of passage to the First Miners' Chamber. The roof rises to 6 m and the walls spread to a width of 10 m, while the stream emerges from a boulder pile which rises steeply and almost blocks the way on. There is a way through but it is a wet climb through squeezes between boulders, and off-route the boulders are dangerously loose. So the caves beyond, of no great length, are for cavers only, fully equipped and with knowledge of the route. Upwards, the cone of boulders, descending from the break in the roof, probably continues to the surface 70 m above – it appears to be the bottom end of a massive choked sinkhole with soil and vegetation obscuring any surface sign.

The chamber, 400 m in from the entrance, makes a positive ending for the easily accessible part of Dow Cave. So return to daylight and appreciate again this magnificent stretch of stream cave; both the wide bedding section, with the pool, and the downstream canyon are on a bold scale and provide some of the finest accessible cave scenery in the country. A visit to Dow is both fascinating and exciting.

The cave is on private land, but the landowner places no restriction on reasonable access.

31 – Kilnsey Crag   974682

It is impossible to think of limestone crags in the Yorkshire Dales without including Kilnsey Crag. This most distinctively shaped crag, with its dramatic overhang, is one of the best-known features along the length of Wharfedale. Perhaps its only disadvantage is that it is hardly a venue for walkers, as it is beside the road, and even the best view of it is from the car window.

The Crag, or Scar as it used to be known, is an imposing chunk of limestone. While less than 300 m long and little over 40 m high, the tremendous overhangs which project some 10 m are unmatched on any other British crag. Carved in massive, almost white limestone, Kilnsey Crag changes in mood at around midday; before then the rock can be bright and warm in the morning sun, but in the afternoon it lies dark and sombre in deep shadow. But at any time the profiles of the overhangs, seen from either end, cannot fail to impress.

Kilnsey Crag owes its existence to glaciation. During each of the Ice Ages, powerful valley glaciers swept down both Wharfedale and Littondale. The original valleys were cut by rivers and tended to follow a curved or meandering course; where Kilnsey now stands the pre-glacial valley was bent round to the east. But glaciers, being less flexible than rivers, prefer a straighter line, and heading down Wharfedale they soon trimmed off the bend around Kilnsey. The Crag is therefore described as a truncated spur, and is a landform indicative of the glacial history of the valley. With such a clear glacial origin, Kilnsey Crag is not really a limestone feature; but the strength of the rock, together with limestone's resistance to surface water erosion, accounts for the Crag being perhaps the most spectacular truncated spur in the country.

The last glacier retreated from Wharfedale only about 15,000 years ago, as the climate finally warmed up after the cold of the last Ice Age. As the snout of the glacier melted back, it left a retreat moraine, a barrier of boulder clay across the floor of the dale at Mill Scar Lash waterfall, 2 km down from Kilnsey. Meltwater

The main overhang of Kilnsey Crag

accumulated behind the moraine and formed a lake reaching back to the confluence of the Wharfe and the Skirfare. But the lake was short-lived; it filled with silts and had its outlet lowered through the moraine. The consequence is the very flat floor of the valley between Kilnsey and Conistone.

The combination of the flat lakebed, with the towering Crag and the strong springs at its foot, always made Kilnsey a landmark in Wharfedale. Iron Age settlements on the valley floor date back around 2000 years but there is little sign of them now. Kilnsey really became of importance in the twelfth century when it was a key centre of the great Pennine estates owned by Fountains Abbey. Mastiles Lane was the main sheep drovers' road; it can now be traced as a green track from the back of the village right across Malham Moor and over to Ribblesdale. Sheep were brought from all over the moor down to Kilnsey for shearing. Following the dissolution of the monasteries, Kilnsey Hall was built in 1648 as the centre of the community. It is a splendid building, its grandeur still recognisable even though today it is only used as a barn; it is tucked away behind the Tennant Arms, the much more recent inn which is so picturesquely framed by the Crag when seen from the south. Still a feature of Kilnsey is the Show held every summer on the old lakebed fields in front of the inn. Traditional events feature strongly at the Show, with sheepdog trials, horse racing and dry-stone walling competitions.

A highlight of the Kilnsey Show is always the Crag Race – the energetic way to rush to the top of the Crag and back. A variety of poorly marked paths do reach up at either end of the Crag, but they can hardly be recommended for a walk. The brow of the Crag is not high enough to form a notable viewpoint, and the grass slopes away dangerously towards the overhang. It is much better to walk to the eastern slopes of Wharfedale, and let Kilnsey Crag take the stage in a splendid panorama, for then it can really be appreciated.

32 – Conistone Dib   982674

Conistone is a charming and peaceful village tucked away from the main road on the east side of Wharfedale. The slopes above the village are fine open limestone country, and a pair of small gorges provide the key to a very pleasant circular walk.

A track, signposted between the houses, is the way out of the south end of the village, and it climbs steadily and easily, obliquely up the hillside. There are fine views back over the rooftops of the village and across the floor of Wharfedale to the looming cliffs of Kilnsey Crag. On the immediate left of the track low grassy mounds are all that is left of the waste piles from bygone quarrying when a good bed of limestone was worked by hand for use in the local building. Fortunately no modern larger venture has followed, and further up the hill the natural limestone scars are progressively more rugged. At the fourth gate ignore the farmer's tractor tracks going up the hill, and follow the path which almost contours until it rises over a small bluff and drops into the Dib Scar valley.

Back at the tail-end of the Ice Ages, less than 15,000 years ago, the deep-frozen ground prevented drainage sinking even into the limestone, and meltwater coursed down the hillsides into Wharfedale. In the meltwater channel down here one particularly strong bed of limestone created a waterfall which retreated into the hillside as the abrasive sediment-laden water ate at the rock. And so Dib Scar was created – a tapering retreat gorge rimmed by limestone cliffs and headed by the overhanging rock of the 20 m high waterfall, now permanently dry as the headwaters have long sunk into the unfrozen limestone. It is often described as a miniature Malham Cove with its dry valley feeding from the fells above.

The path skirts the rim of Dib Scar, crosses the valley at its head and then ascends a steep bank on its way south. The third stile leads on to the open grassland; leave the main path, to head north-east to a stile which takes the Dales Way over the next dry-stone wall. This is one of the newer long-distance paths which here takes the high road above Wharfedale through a stretch of sweeping country sculpted in grand style by ancient glaciers.

Away to the left there are some impressive areas of bare limestone pavement formed on massive dipping slabs of bedrock, and there is a low scar right beside the path. Step up the few metres on to the scar for it is just the edge of a small but very fine piece of limestone pavement. Since the ice scraped clean its overburden, rainwater has fretted the limestone on a bold scale; deep rounded fissures, or grykes, separate the solid clints of bedrock. Look closely at the limestone, for practically all the surfaces are covered by lichens; this is significant because they largely account for the rounding of the clints as opposed to the sharp fretted sculpture which rainwater carves on totally unvegetated limestone. Mosses also grow but only under the shadowy arms of a pair of trees, for they cannot survive the sun on the bare exposed rock.

An old limekiln further along the path serves as a reminder of past activities in the area. A century and more ago the slopes east of Wharfedale were host to a range of industry – lime-burning, stone-winning, peat-cutting and, higher up the fells, lead-mining. Men of the valley floor villages trekked daily up the hills to work, but today they are followed only by the sheep farmers, and the walkers who come purely for recreation.

As the path continues north, it provides distant views ahead into the glaciated trough of Littondale, and eventually an excellent view down Conistone Dib. This is a classic example of a limestone dry valley. Like Dib Scar, it is an old meltwater channel but is on a much larger scale; it must have carried a large stream perhaps fed for a time by a lobe of wasting glacier on the plateau above. At the head of the ravine, a couple of stiles guide the way to a rocky descent, which is the site of an ancient cascade where the meltwater carved through some stronger beds of limestone. The going becomes easier where the rockfall and scree are left behind and the valley opens out into a wider trough with a grassy floor and just a few crags high on the left. But further down the sides close in, as the valley approaches the same stronger beds of limestone which form Dib Scar. There is no old waterfall in Conistone Dib; instead the channel narrows to a rock gorge, often known as Gurling Trough, cut deeply into the stronger limestone. At one point the vertical walls are less than a metre apart, scoured and polished by the glacial

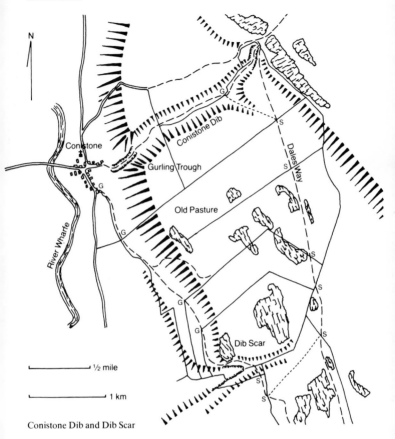

Conistone Dib and Dib Scar

waters of yesteryear; it is fortunate indeed that the water now flows underground for if it was still on the surface the gorge would be inaccessible.

The gorge descends steadily, before it starts to open out, drops over some steps which are the remnant of old quarrying, and then dies out right at the edge of Conistone village. Limestone makes the countryside around Conistone, both the scars and pavements on the tops and also the rock walls of the gorges down below. The modern drainage is all underground, and unseen in this area; but the climatic changes of the past, by sometimes allowing both water and ice to carve the surface, account for much of the landscape of today.

All of this walk is on public footpaths.

33 – Mossdale Scar   982677

The rolling expanse of moors between Wharfedale and Nidderdale forms one of the largest blocks of roadless country in the Yorkshire Pennines. Grassington Moor towards the south has been pock-marked by three centuries of lead-mining, now only a feature of the past. Northwards the slopes rise to Great Whernside. But isolated in the heart of Conistone Moor, a powerful beck finds limestone and disappears into Mossdale Scar.

Conistone village is the best place to start a walk to Mossdale, because the old Bycliffe Road provides easy going. Many years ago this was a packhorse route over to Nidderdale, though it must have been a rigorous trail during the winter months. It gained more travellers when it gave access to the Mossdale lead-mines, and was later used to reach the peat hags which were worked for fuel. Today the lower end of the road is tarred as far as the Wassa Hill TV mast, but beyond there it is normally impassable to anything less than a Landrover; and the farmers and the gamekeeper hardly provide heavy traffic.

On the walk up from the floor of Wharfedale, there are fine views behind, across to Kilnsey Crag. To either side of the road there is dry limestone country providing good pasture, but further up the grassland is broken by white rock scars – the first descriptively named Hill Castles Scar. Above the second scar, limestone pavements stretch in each direction, relics of the stronger beds of rock swept clean by the Wharfedale glacier of the last Ice Age. The road continues to climb and then crosses on to the outcrops of the

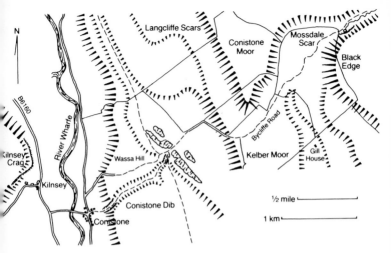

From Kilnsey Crag to Mossdale Scar

sandstones which overlie the Great Scar Limestone. Across Kelber Moor there are few rock outcrops, just a rolling plateau with its veneer of boulder clay. The sweet fescue grasses of the limestone country are gone; green is replaced by brown, as heather and coarse mat grass thrive on the sandy soils.

Down into the broad, shallow valley of Gill House Beck the walk is across true gritstone country. It can be awfully bleak and wild, but on a sunny day can be a delight – silent, expansive and far enough from roads to ensure that the walker normally has it to himself. Ahead, the crags of Black Edge are anonymous from a distance. They are in fact one of the Yoredale limestones tucked into a sequence of sandstones and shales – and there lies the secret of Mossdale Scar. Round a gentle corner, Mossdale Beck comes into sight, flowing down from the north to disappear into a tumbled heap of limestone blocks. Above the sink the scar rises for 15 m, extending less than 200 m, but an oasis of limestone in a harsh moor of gritstone.

This magnificent setting for a disappearing stream had to attract the attention of cavers, and in 1941 an entrance was found between the boulders of the collapsed scar. The stream passage inside is low and wide, an ominous place with inky black water swirling between black limestone walls. Unfortunately the stream can only be followed for 400 m before it is lost into a waterlogged fissure, and the next place it is seen is at the Black Keld resurgence on the floor of Wharfedale just south of Kettlewell. Therein lies the mystery of Mossdale, for the beck sinks into one limestone and rises from another; somewhere beneath Conistone Moor the water finds its way through two beds of sandstone, probably through faults that have fractured the insoluble rock. That main stream route is inaccessible, but there are other passages which continue beyond where the water is lost. The most significant carries a tiny stream along the base of the limestone bed, and because it has a resistant sandstone floor it has never been enlarged beyond the size of a constricted crawlway. The Marathon Passage is a kilometre of interminable crawling, twisting and turning; only at the far end of this arduous crawl are roomy caverns which unfortunately end in boulder chokes deep beneath the southern end of Black Edge.

Mossdale Caverns were always famous, both for the mystery of the streamway and the severity of the long crawls. But they also achieved infamy on the saddest day in British caving. On 24 June 1967, six young, experienced cavers died in Mossdale. Marathon Passage acts as an overflow route from the main streamway, and because it is so small it is rapidly filled to the roof by a flood pulse down the main stream. On that June afternoon, a storm of unforgettable intensity turned the sinking beck into a raging torrent. The flood overflow built into a wall of water as it swept down the confines of Marathon Passage. And the fates were against those cavers because the water met them part-way along the crawl on their return journey. All six drowned. A plaque above the sealed entrance at the left end of the scar commemorates that sad day, and Mossdale Scar provides its own natural monument.

Leaving this lonely spot, the walker can return the way he came. But it is better to leave the old road just below the main limestone pavements, and turn left to pick up the path which returns down the

The sinking stream at Mossdale Scar

ravine of Conistone Dib (and which is described under the previous walk). For the more energetic, follow any of the footpaths which loop north of the Bycliffe Road, to take in the staircase of limestone scars which rises from Wharfedale to Conistone Moor. For those with transport from Kettlewell, the walk along the whole length of the Langcliffe Scars is one of the more splendid high-level routes in the Dales. But even without that diversion, the route from Wharfedale to the isolated Mossdale Scar introduces the walker to a new dimension of the Yorkshire Pennines. A touch of gritstone creates a worthy addition to the walks on limestone country.

Bycliffe Road is a public right of way, and the other routes are all on public footpaths. There is no access into Mossdale Caverns.

34 – Stump Cross Caverns   088635

East of Wharfedale there is little limestone exposed at the surface.
It lies beneath the grit expanse of Grassington Moor and dips down
so that most of it even misses the floor of Nidderdale. The Middle
Craven Fault cuts east-west just south of Grassington, and south of
it the limestone is far beneath the surface where grits rise to the
summit of Simon Seat. But between these two grit moors there is a
tongue of limestone. South of Grassington it forms the reef knolls of
Elbolton, Kail and other hills – mounds of calcite bound together on
the sea floor by algae and coral millions of years ago, and now
giving their shape to these isolated limestone hills. And east of the
two lovely villages of Burnsall and Appletreewick, an anticlinal
upfold of limestone is exposed as far as Greenhow Hill.

The limestone betrays its presence by the dry valley of Dry Gill,
partly followed by the road from Grassington to Pateley Bridge.
Higher up the valley the stream of Mongo Gill sinks into the
limestone and there are various resurgences lower down. Some of
these are in Troller's Gill, a narrower and deeper section of the
valley with some scars of bare limestone and almost warranting
description as a gorge. Between Dry Gill and Greenhow Hill, the
limestone attracted lead-miners as long ago as Roman times. The
rich mineral veins supported a thriving industry which climaxed
early in the nineteenth century but which had almost died by the
end of it.

In 1858, lead-miners broke into a series of natural caves close to
an old boundary post known as Stump Cross. Such accidental
discovery of caves was not uncommon, but these passages were
unusually well decorated with stalagmites, and some were later
opened as a show cave. Today's visitors walk round the caves at
their own pace, for there are no guided tours. While this means that
the best formations have to be behind protective grilles, it does let
the visitor stop and look just where he wants and can give young
children a sense of exploration especially in some of the smaller
passages.

The caverns are entered from a flight of steps, the lower part of
which follows a natural rift. The path continues into a level tunnel,

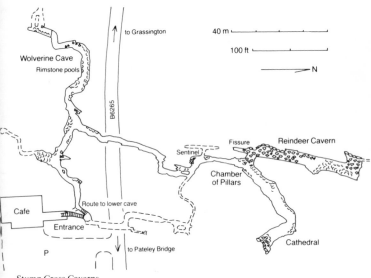

Stump Cross Caverns

past a side gallery almost blocked by stalactites and stalagmites, and then between banks of massive calcite flowstone. Gravel deposits covered with layers of stalagmite are a feature of the cave, and many of the paths have been trenched through them to allow upright walking. Turn right at the junction and then cast a glance at the roof. It is irregular, pitted with solution pockets and domes, and broken by solution rifts on the lines of joints. Clearly, to create roof solution features on this scale, the passage must have been originally full of water; indeed it is an excellent example of a phreatic cave – in other words, one that was formed below the water table in the limestone. Today the water table is far below, for the hill has been drained due to the deepening of Dry Gill; there are five other distinct levels in the whole 6 km complex of the Stump Cross cave system reflecting progressive falls in the water table during the complex of erosion stages through the period of the Ice Ages.

The end of Wolverine Cave in Stump Cross Caverns

Further along the passage there are more calcite formations, of which the largest is the column known as the Sentinel: a white stalactite curtain has grown down 2 m to join on to a rounded stalagmite boss. At the Chamber of Pillars a boulder pile supports more stalagmite columns, and the passage enlarges till it is 5 m wide. It continues, dotted with stalagmites, and then rounds a corner to where the roof rises into the Cathedral Chamber. Its far end is a boulder slope on which stands another fine calcite column; but unlike the Sentinel this one is a stalagmite which has grown upwards till it met the roof.

A continuation of the large tunnel lies behind the boulder pile at the Chamber of Pillars. It is known as Reindeer Cavern and is another spacious chamber decorated with stalagmites. At present it is inaccessible, but there are plans to drive a short tunnel and extend the show cave path into it in the near future. Its name derives from the mass of reindeer bones which were found in the fissure above the boulder pile. Wild reindeer once roamed these hills and some fell down an open rift into the cave before it was sealed and covered by sediments from the glaciers of the last Ice Age.

Back towards the entrance, Wolverine Cave is a major side passage. Here again the path was cut through banks of sediment and calcite, and this produced two great benefits. Firstly it uncovered a host of bone material belonging to wolverine and various other animals. The wolverine was a carnivore who probably lived in the cave during one of the Pleistocene cold periods, which must have been more than 100,000 years ago because that is the age of the stalagmite which encrusts some of the bones. The second benefit of the trenched path is that it gives an eye-level view of the gour pools which once formed the passage floor, and which now adorn a convenient ledge. The pools are now dry, but their deposits remain and it is obvious why they are also known as rimstone pools; thin walls of rippling calcite once rimmed pools in which tiny crystals and rounded calcite masses developed. The passage ends with a view of a particularly fine grotto of stalagmites and stalactites, but look also at the roof nearby where delicate calcite straws are so close that you can see the drops of water on the end of each one.

Some of the best bone material is on display in the café at the cave entrance because it had to be moved from the cave. It adds much to the story of Stump Cross Caverns – not just a story of cave formation many hundreds of thousands of years ago, but also one which continues to reveal something of the Pennine wildlife through the changing times of the Ice Ages.

The cave is open daily from Easter to November and on Sundays through the winter.

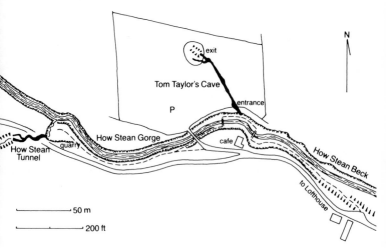

How Stean Gorge

the gorge has vertical walls dropping 10 m into almost still, black water, its surface broken only by the trickles of water seeping from the limestone. It's a lovely sight, especially when it catches some sun between its deep shadows. Just to the left, How Stean Tunnel is a cave carrying a tributary to the beck. It is a tall twisting canyon right through from the sink just beyond the road; but it is hardly worth the slippery climb down into it, and there is a pool too deep for wellingtons part-way along. The rock platform where the path ends is the floor of an old quarry, and one wall of the cave passage was long ago removed when the quarrymen worked right up to it.

Downstream the path continues underneath the road bridge by following a natural niche cut in the limestone wall. It is just high enough for a stooping walk and leads to a footbridge over to the far bank, giving a good view along the gorge. Right beside the path, a bank of calcareous tufa is still being built up by lime-saturated water seeping out of the limestone. Tiny plants and mosses grow on the tufa; by taking the carbon dioxide out of the water they cause even more calcite to be precipitated. Just beyond the tufa, the entrance to

Tom Taylor's Cave opens into the gorge wall, and below it the path descends to another bridge and continues on to a broad slab of limestone just above water level. The gorge opens out further down and loses its depth, but it is worth going down on to those limestone slabs which are so beautifully scalloped by eddies in the water which once ran over them.

Tom Taylor's Cave provides an interesting alternative route back, and all it requires of the visitor is a reasonable torch. The passage starts as a tall narrow canyon, and wooden steps lead down to the tiny cave stream which drains through a lower fissure out to the beck. Upstream and rising slightly, the cave is almost straight as it follows a joint in the limestone. There are no real obstacles, and it is one of the very few caves where it is safe to let adventurous young children explore ahead and probe the darkness with their own torches. The only junction is where the roof rises into a small chamber, and daylight can be seen up the right-hand exit which is the easier way to the surface. Both branches emerge in a rocky depression at the top end of the car park field. There are other cave entrances nearby, but they are all low and muddy so remain just for the cavers. Inside them, the passages do increase in size, and carry a small stream down through the hillside parallel to the gorge; it is fed by leakage from the surface bed at the top of the gorge. Tom Taylor's was once part of that system, but the surface gorge has continued to carry most of the water, so developing to a larger scale and leaving the caves here as rather poor relations.

Victorian tourists dubbed the area 'Little Switzerland', but that name does credit to neither Switzerland nor the gorge. How Stean Beck has no Alpine scenery, but it has carved out a textbook example of a limestone gorge. Though smaller than many others in Britain, it is still alive because the local geology has not allowed its water to disappear underground easily enough to fossilise it.

The gorge is on private land; it is open all through the year and tickets for access are obtained at the café.

36 – Goyden Pot   100762

The River Nidd has its headwaters on the eastern slopes of Great
Whernside. It drains east, through the Angram and Scar House
reservoirs and then south to Pateley Bridge down the lovely glacial
trough of Nidderdale. But just below the turn to the south, the
entire river sinks underground and next sees the light of day at Nidd
Heads, powerful springs more than 3 km away just south of
Lofthouse village. Underground, it flows through a series of
passages as yet only partially explored, but including Goyden Pot.

Except for the very hardy fell-walker, the approach to Goyden
Pot has to be up Nidderdale. The road from Pateley Bridge on its
way into Lofthouse almost passes over Nidd Heads. High walls
don't help the motorist to see and there's no place to stop, but the
river flows away on the left of the road while there is no sign of it on
the right. There's little to see even for those who do stop; the water
just pours from low cave openings which can only be penetrated for
more than a few metres by the cave-divers. In Lofthouse itself the
road crosses a bridge over a dry riverbed, a sure sign of the caves
that lie beneath. A private road, signposted to the Scar House
Reservoirs, continues up the valley; now open to visitors, it is only
narrow, but is smoothly curved and evenly graded, for it follows the
railway line which was laid to transport materials during the
construction of the dams.

Riverbed exposures are clearly of sandstone, for the underlying
limestone is completely beneath the valley floor along this stretch; it
is only exposed at the surface at the two ends of the valley where the
River Nidd sinks and then resurges. A small stream flows down the
oversize riverbed, and on either side of the valley dark edges break
the slopes rising to the heather-covered moors – all typical of
sandstone country. Just beyond Limley Farm, a picnic area on the
left provides a convenient spot to park. Visible from the road, a scar
of white rock adjacent to the riverbed shows the presence of
limestone, right at the entrance to Goyden Pot.

In normal weather, the riverbed is dry. The water sinks a few
hundred metres further upstream, and then flows through another
cave (which is however rather muddy). Down to Goyden Pot the

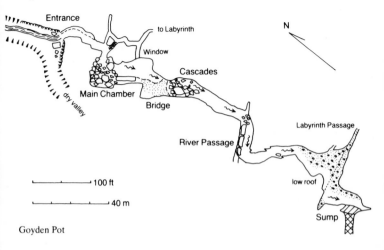

Goyden Pot

riverbed is a floor of washed boulders; the normal sinks are too
constricted to absorb high flood levels and overflow water then
continues down to go underground in the Goyden Pot entrance.
Downstream of Goyden Pot the riverbed is floored with grass, and
overflow due to complete flooding of Goyden Pot is a rare event.
The Goyden entrance, a cave really, not a pothole, yawns black in
the white cliff. On no account should it be entered when any stream
is flowing into it, for that indicates a potential rapid expansion into a
river. It is an awesome sight when the river does flow into Goyden
Pot; the water sluices down the entrance passage at great speed.
Any temptation to climb along the ledges should be strongly
resisted – nothing more can be seen, the ledges get thinner and
more slippery, and anyone falling in would be swept away and
almost certainly drowned.

If the entrance is completely dry, Goyden Pot is well worth a visit
and can be partly explored with a good strong torch for every
person. Curving away from daylight, the entrance passage is 3 m
high and wide; polished and scalloped white rock is swept clean by
the periodic flooding. Eyes slowly adjust to the dark, and a few

minutes scrambling leads to a triple junction. Ahead the passage is blocked by a tangle of vegetation and great tree trunks, testimony to the violent flooding. Left is a tube which leads off to a maze of dry passages where it becomes progressively easier to get lost (and anyone venturing in should be aware of the sudden drop from the Window into the Main Chamber below). The way on is to the right, usually over a pair of jammed tree trunks, ducking under a rock arch and on to some massive boulders where the passage opens out. A dull rumble is the first sign that the underground River Nidd is not far away.

The boulders are massive slabs of bedrock which have fallen from the roof over the long periods of geological time; both slabs and roof are now stable. The Main Chamber extends ahead and down to the left. Scrambling down over the breakdown blocks is quite safe as long as care is taken to find the right route which avoids any dangerous jumping; if in doubt keep to the right. Lower down, the floor of the chamber comes into sight with the river crossing from left to right, cascading over more breakdown. There is one conspicuously large tilted block, and an easy way down to its right keeps against the wall, where a sloping ledge leads to a flat sandy floor with blocks of insoluble black chert projecting from the dark limestone. The level section of floor extends over a rock bridge which spans the river. Tread warily towards the downstream side, because there is a vertical drop to the water, but there is also a fine view out into the blackness of the downstream river passage – a large noisy tunnel carrying the Nidd to greater depths.

To follow the river downstream it is necessary to climb down the cascades which pass under the rock bridge. A careful choice of route keeps the visitor dry unless the river is in spate, but proper caving equipment, in the form of helmet-mounted lamps, is needed to leave both hands free for the climbs over the boulders. Below the cascades there are pools which require knee-deep wading and the gradient of the passage eases off. It continues as a spectacular cave canyon, around 5 m wide, with the water right across the floor. There are no stalactites, only bands of projecting chert to break the greys and blacks of the polished limestone walls. The roof is a sloping bedding plane, and round a few corners it comes

The River Passage in Goyden Pot

progressively lower. It is only at stooping height across a wide bank of cobbles, before it lifts briefly and then slopes down into an inky sump pool where the water escapes beneath the surface.

Side passages there are, but they lead into complex galleries which should only be visited by fully equipped cavers. Lacking helmets and caving lamps, most visitors will turn back at the bridge in the Main Chamber. Climb back up the boulders keeping to the left wall, but be prepared to follow the wall well round at the top of the chamber; the exit passage is over to the right, and is not too obvious behind a large slab. Though it is a short underground journey only as far as the rock bridge, it is a worthwhile one; the sight, sound and feel of the underground river in the darkness of

Goyden Pot is dramatic indeed and much more appreciated than any stream in a well-lit show cave.

The Yorkshire Water Authority charges for the use of the road by cars, but there is no further restriction on access to Goyden Pot, except by flooding.

37 – Hardrow Force   867912

Wensleydale has always been a bit of a backwater. It does have a long history of settlement: Castle Dykes, near Aysgarth, is a Bronze Age earthwork, Bainbridge has its Roman fort built on a drumlin of glacial debris, and it was famous for its hunting forests in the Middle Ages. But industry has tended to pass it by. Woollen mills thrived in the nineteenth century but could not last into modern times, and lead-mining in the dale never matched up to the areas north and south. Before the turnpike came through the valley in 1795, it never had more than a packhorse trail. The railway came, but closed in 1954, and today the main road only really goes from nowhere to nowhere. Though it lies in the Yorkshire Dales National Park, it is away from the popular areas around Malham and the Three Peaks, so it remains a gentle farming landscape with not too many visitors.

Wensleydale is well known for its cheese, and dairy produce is still the cornerstone of farming on the floor of the dale. While centuries ago the cheeses were made each summer on the individual farms, they are now produced in large creameries, one of which is in Hawes. The dale is equally well known to geologists, for its original name is Yoredale – it carries the River Ure, even though the name Wensleydale (after the old market town of Wensley) has been in use since the twelfth century. The old name is preserved in the geological record where the Yoredale Series is a distinctive and well-known group of rocks dating back about 300 million years to Carboniferous times. The Series consists of repeated cycles of limestone, shale and sandstone which accumulated in shallow seas where rhythmic subsidence and deposition accounted for the variations in sediments. In total they are about 400 m thick, and,

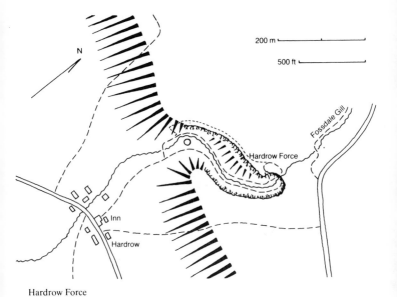

Hardrow Force

lying almost horizontally, they form virtually the entire slopes of Wensleydale.

It is the Yoredale Series which has given Wensleydale a very distinctive landscape. The dale has been cut over a million or more years by the action of both rivers and glaciers, but almost everywhere the slopes still show the influence of the alternations of the rock types, most significantly the contrast between strong limestone and weak shale. The beds of limestone, and there are about ten of them, are mostly less than 10 m thick but they are strong enough to form the scars, ledges and terraces which are diagnostic of Yoredale country. From almost any viewpoint in Wensleydale the stepped profile of the slopes is clearly recognisable, and the bands of limestone can be counted down the hillside. The same profile has also been imposed on the streams and rivers which drain into the dale. The limestone outcrops are too narrow to have allowed much cave development, so the main drainage has stayed on the surface, but a limestone cap to a thick bed of shale provides the perfect site for a waterfall. Wensleydale is the valley of waterfalls, and highest of all is Hardrow Force.

The tiny hamlet of Hardrow, or Hardraw as it is sometimes known, lies just north of Hawes. Hardrow Force lies just behind the church where a small river flows over Hardrow Scar, a rock terrace formed by what is now known as the Hardraw Scar Limestone; the contrast in spelling is now permanently ingrained in the literature. The way to the waterfall is through the hallway of the Green Dragon Inn, and emerging from the back of the inn, the geology of the scene is instantly obvious, with the step up to the limestone terrace straight ahead. The path stays level and heads for a wooded niche in the scar, which is the mouth of a short gorge formed by the headward retreat of the waterfall. Past the remains of a stone bandstand, where brass band contests were once held because of the good acoustics of the gorge, the path follows the stream round a gentle bend to the first and best view of the Force. A stark rock wall lines a great amphitheatre and from the lip on the far side the stream drops into a round plunge pool. Hardrow Force is 27 m high and is therefore claimed as the highest completely free-drop waterfall in England – though that excludes the various underground waterfalls in the Ingleborough area. Regardless of records, it is an impressive sight.

In the wall behind the waterfall, the rocks are beautifully exposed and are a classic example of a Yoredale cycle. At the top there is nearly 10 m of thinly bedded black limestone; the stream has cut part-way down through the limestone, but it still forms the lip of the fall and its base is clearly recognisable by a massive overhang. Beneath it there is about 5 m of strong sandstone, with two thick beds, recognisable by patches of rusty weathering, grading downward into progressively more shaley beds. This is typical of the Yoredale rocks, which are a sedimentary record of a small delta bringing first mud and then more and more sand into the basin of deposition, before the water again cleared to allow formation of the limestone.

Hardrow Force in very dry conditions

Overhangs above the easily eroded shale leave plenty of room for the footpath to curve right round behind the waterfall. Much of the path is over sandstone blocks which have fallen from above, but parts are slippery where showers emerge from the limestone roof and banks of broken shale are slowly weathering to wet mud. The main stream lands 10 m out from the back wall, and it is a mesmerising sight standing in the dry as the water shoots out overhead. On a dry day, when the stream is low, it is a comfortable spot; but return after a heavy rainstorm. Transformed into a powerful torrent, the cascade crashes into the plunge pool and scours it clean of debris. Spray lashes around the amphitheatre, and it is easy to understand the powers of erosion that created the gorge and waterfall as it now stands. Nearly all the stream erosion takes place in the few days each year of flood flow; only when seen under these conditions is it really conceivable how the Force has managed to retreat the 250 m length of its gorge. And it has taken around 14,000 years to do so, since the time when the last Ice Age glaciers melted away from Wensleydale and the beck first flowed over the limestone edge of Hardraw Scar.

Between drought and flood the force has many moods, and it can often be worth a return visit. A rare contrast is provided by a winter hard enough to freeze the Force. In 1881 it was turned into a column of ice 3 m in diameter with a fringe of massive icicles, but since then it was only the cold winter of 1963 which provided a repeat of the spectacle.

Beyond the back of the Force, the path continues round and then down a flight of steps and along to a footbridge. From the top of the steps another path zig-zags up a gulley cut into the main cliff. It is well made with large flagstone slabs for steps – a relic of Victorian days when Hardraw Force was a popular tourist spot but access had to be made easy for ladies in broad and flowing dresses. At the top of the steps, keep to the right and follow the flagstone path 100 m through the woods to the lip of the Force. The upstream valley is shallow as the beck has only managed to cut a few metres down into its limestone bed before it drops off into space. There is no fence around the edge of the drop, so great care is needed on the polished rock, but there is a fine view down into the amphitheatre cut by the falls. The path ends on a block of rock, just right of the lip of the fall, and it is not recommended to stand on it; the limestone is too well jointed and the overhang is considerable. Some winter's day in the next few years, that block of rock will crash to the edge of the plunge pool. That is, after all, the natural process by which the whole gorge was cut.

Hardrow Force is on private land, and is only accessible through the Green Dragon Inn on payment of a small fee.

38 – Aysgarth Falls   012887

Waterfalls may well be a characteristic of Wensleydale, but the best known of all the dale's cascades – Aysgarth Falls – is ironically the least typical. For a start it carries the entire River Ure over its rocky terraces, so the sheer volume of water heightens its spectacle. And secondly it is cut almost entirely in limestone without the thick shale beds to create the overhangs which typify the other Wensleydale waterfalls. The name is also a slight misnomer because there are three separate falls, so that a visit to them all requires walking over a kilometre of very lovely river scenery. For all that, the falls are a justifiably popular feature, and though they attract perhaps too many people on a warm summer Sunday, they can be seen without the crowds on most days of the year.

Signposted from Aysgarth village, and on the north side of the river, the National Park has a car park and information centre which is the obvious starting point for any visitor. The falls are best seen from top to bottom, so leave the centre through the car park and down the path signed to the upper falls. These consist of a wide double cascade, each drop of about 2 m over individual beds of strong dark limestone. Look closely at the limestone where the bed comes to the river's edge, for there are fine colonies of the fossil corals Lithostrotion and also many of the large scallop shells of Productus. On the far bank, a thick bed of black shale can be seen above the lighter and obviously stronger limestone – and therein lies the reason for the falls' existence. Ice Age glaciers swept down

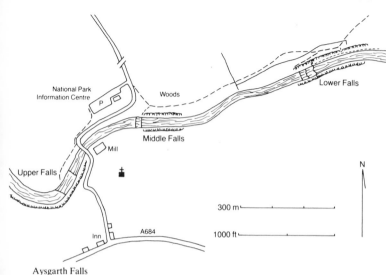

National Park
Information Centre

P

Woods

Lower Falls

Middle Falls

Mill

Upper Falls

N

A684

Inn

300 m

1000 ft

Aysgarth Falls

Wensleydale and smoothed the profile of its floor almost regardless
of the type of bedrock. Since the glacial retreat, the river has
continued the erosion but has had much more success removing the
weak shale than the strong limestone. So the shale has largely gone
from the river bed, while the series of limestones, gently dipping
upstream, remain as steps and create all the falls of Aysgarth.

Immediately above the falls a low weir of timber separates the
rapids from calm water and was built to divert water into a mill race
on the far bank, feeding the Yore Mill. Retrace the footpath
downstream and join the road just after its rather fine bridge. The
mill, directly across the river, was originally built for the cotton
industry in 1784, but failed, fell into disuse and was then destroyed
by fire. The present building dates from 1853 when it became a
woollen mill and supplied the wool for the original balaclava
helmets of the Crimean War. Later it became a flour mill and today
it is a carriage museum. The tailrace of the millstream yawns dry

where it opens back into the river swirling down to the next
falls.

Follow the road for a while and then join the main path
signposted to the lower and middle falls, avoiding the paths lower in
the woods which really cannot stand the erosive trampling of many
feet. Even from the main path, the middle falls cannot be missed.
Just home in on their muffled roar, and there is a viewpoint from
where they are easily seen – 5 m high with a wide vertical drop over
a strong bed of limestone followed by a staircase down thinner beds
of the same rock.

Return to the higher path through the Freeholders' Wood. Hazel
trees dominate with their straight, branch-free trunks which were
so easily cut for poles, but there is also a scatter of birch and other
species. The path has suffered from too many visitors, but follow it
through a kissing gate, where the sound of rapids can be heard
below, and stay up through the open field. Through another gate,
the path divides close to the rim of 10 m high cliffs. Go first
downstream, and just before the main path turns away scramble
down an obvious gully to the riverbed.

Almost level limestone slabs extend in both directions, though
how much of them is visible depends on the flow at the time.
Upstream the slabs reach to the foot of the lower falls – an 8 m high
succession of cascades with again the highest steps at the top in
response to the repeated pattern of bed thicknesses in the
limestone. On either side the walls overhang where the strong upper
limestones stand proud of the lower weaker beds. This shallow
gorge is only 10 m deep but it is 50 m wide and its length of perhaps
300 m shows how far the falls have retreated since the glaciers gave
way to the River Ure. The black, thin bedded limestones which
form the riverbed look dirty and impure. But in fact their colour is
only due to a tiny proportion of carbon and their purity is
demonstrated by the abundance of fossil coral colonies – for the
corals only grew in the clearest of seas.

At times of low water there is a wide expanse of bare rock
upstream to the falls. It is like a gigantic pegboard; carved by a
combination of solution by river water and grinding action by the
river cobbles, there are hundreds of potholes, or moulins as they

The lower falls at Aysgarth

may be called, mostly less than a metre across. River water
continually pours into some of them, and then escapes through
miniature caves along flooded bedding planes back to the main
channel; because the bedrock is limestone the river water is always
trying to short-cut through caves, but with its large flow and low
gradient the River Ure will never go completely underground in
Wensleydale. The low cliffs beside the riverbed are hardly stable,
and blocks of limestone are falling out of many sections. Yet at one
point, a tiny spring is depositing a layer of white tufa over the
bedrock – another case of nature vying with itself by eroding the
cliffs with one hand and reinforcing them with the other.

Due to the overhang, there is no safe or easy climb by the falls, so
return downstream to the same route out – even though the gully is

not so easily spotted from below. Back on the main path, divert for just a few steps to see the lower falls from above, and so complete a walk through the best of Wensleydale's river scenery.

The paths have unrestricted free access, but there is a small charge for car parking.

39 – The Buttertubs   875962

Streams of water cascading to oblivion down vertically sided potholes are mainly features of the high and remote limestone fells, merely because they lie in the top of the limestone beds. Most such potholes are therefore only in the province of the fell-walker; however, the Buttertubs are different because they are right at the roadside. They are nonetheless fine shafts and are worthy of a brief stop on a Dales tour.

There's not much sign of limestone along the Buttertubs Pass road as it wends it way over the high ridge between Wensleydale and Swaledale. Plenty of open moorland grazed by sheep, deeply cut stream valleys, and just the occasional rock terrace or white scar; they are all signs of Yoredale country where sandstone and shales dominate and the limestones lie only in thin bands. Some of the fellside streams disappear underground where they cross on to the limestones, and lines of springs commonly mark the bases of the limestone bands. The Buttertubs potholes have been formed where a series of tiny streams meets one of these limestone bands just down the Swaledale side from the top of the pass. By pure chance the line of the road cuts right between the best of the potholes. They are difficult to miss, and there is even car parking space to accommodate the many passers-by.

There are five Buttertubs, all in a row, but the biggest and best are one on each side of the road at the up-valley end of the line. They really are very fine examples of limestone potholes, both nearly 20 m deep and most distinctive because of their complex

The Buttertubs

plan-form. Instead of being simple cylindrical shafts they are deeply fluted into an interconnecting series of slots and shafts separated by narrow pinnacles of limestone bedrock. The horizontal bedding and some vertical joints are easily seen on the limestone walls, and the vertical fluting and ribbing shows where the rock has been slowly dissolved away by falling streams or just dripping water. The potholes have all been formed at the top of the limestone where surface water drains from the shales of the hillside above. The deep fluting of the shaft walls is largely due to the fact that most of this drainage has been just small trickles of very acid and corrosive water out of the boggy vegetation. Under wet conditions, the Buttertubs still swallow small streams today.

The floors of the potholes are covered in stones and cobbles, and the water either filters down between the stones or drains off into narrow cracks in the limestone walls. Only impenetrably narrow cave passages continue below the daylight shafts, but the water can be seen again where it returns to the surface only a short distance away. It is a steep but walkable grassy slope which descends below the Buttertubs to the valley floor. In normal weather conditions, Cliff Beck can be seen flowing away to the north, while the valley floor upstream of the Buttertubs area is dry. The water emerges from Cliff Beck Head Cave, tucked under the bank almost directly below the largest of the Buttertubs. Unfortunately the entrance is not spacious. The stream flows from two passages each less than a metre high, and even they extend only a short distance before becoming too narrow for further progress.

Immediately below the cave sandstone can be seen in the beck floor. That, after all, is why the cave is at that position – the underground stream has quite simply run out of limestone. On the opposite side of the valley water can be seen pouring from a boulder pile concealing another resurgence cave at the same level. But there are not potholes to match the Buttertubs on the hillside just above. Cliff Force Cave lies behind that resurgence and has been explored upstream for more than a kilometre, for its waters drain from the Sargill Beck area on the far side of Stags Fell. These thin bands of Yoredale limestone do account for some peculiar features of cave drainage, and though the Buttertubs waters are only underground for the shortest of distances they have formed an unusually splendid series of pothole shafts.

The Buttertubs lie on open moorland with no access restrictions.

40 – Hell Gill   778963

Legend has it that Dick Turpin once jumped across the gorge of Hell Gill on horseback. In most cases a jump across a 20 m deep gorge would be suicidal or apocryphal, but the limestone ravine of Hell Gill is so narrow that the story becomes credible. There can be few other gorges in Britain, in limestone or any other rock, which

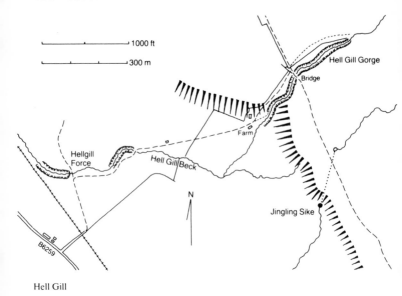

Hell Gill

can match the deep, twisting canyon of this Pennine beck.

Hell Gill Beck drains the eastern side of Mallerstang Common into the headwaters of the River Eden. Only just out of Wensleydale, its geology is not surprisingly the Yoredale rocks, and where the beck crosses each band of limestone it has formed a gorge or waterfall. Being almost on the watershed, the beck forms the county boundary between Yorkshire and Cumbria, and their signboards are the key to finding Hell Gill from the Hawes to Kirkby Stephen road. A farm track turns off to the east and bridges the railway, but it is only a public footpath; there is room to leave cars at the junction. Follow the track over the bridge and then towards the ford across the beck, where the sound of falling water pinpoints Hellgill Force just below the trees. The waterfall forms a curtain over a clear drop of 12 m, and behind it is a perfect section through Yoredale rocks. A thin dark limestone above a rusty sandstone together form the lip of the falls and the lower undercut walls are all in weak shales; it is yet another Niagara-type waterfall so typical of Yoredale country.

Take the track upstream on the south bank of the beck, past a miniature ravine where the stream has cut into the 5 m thick limestone before breaking through it at the Force. Over the bridge, the track cuts across towards the obvious step in the hillside created by the Main Limestone, the thickest in the Yoredale sequence at over 20 m. Hellgill Farm stands just below the step, sited by a limestone spring for its original water supply. The smaller streams off the fell nearly all go underground where they cross the outcrop of the Main Limestone; Jingling Sike, just to the north, flows through a cave 300 m long, but the passage is very small. Hell Gill Beck, however, has such a large flow that it has never managed to sink underground – it has entrenched itself into a deep surface gorge far faster than it could hope to enlarge narrow joints into a cave large enough to swallow it.

Just through the farmyard, the main track climbs up the hill, but turn right where the first tree signposts a narrow path down to the beck at the mouth of the gorge. Dark limestone forms the scars and the walls of the gorge, here little more than 5 m high, and a prominent undercut bedding plane separates it from the sandstone which forms the floor of the beck as far down as a cascade into a pool cut in the underlying shale. Small springs and mossbanks mark the edge of the limestone and it is possible to walk dry into the start of the gorge. From there wellingtons are needed to keep dry and the gorge continues with a fine square profile 5 m wide and 5–10 m deep, until, about 100 m in, a deep pool bars the way.

Return then to follow the path along the north rim of the gorge. Trees right on the edge obscure all views down to the gill, except from Hell Gill Bridge. This fine old stone bridge carried the main road along the dale until 1825 when the turnpike picked out the route of the present main road. Now it carries just a bridleway, but it does permit a glimpse into the depths of the ravine – where a deep narrow pool lies 12 m below the parapet. The path continues up the fell, outside the wall, and rejoins the beck beyond the top of the gorge in a wide valley cut in the next bed of shale. It is worth a scramble down into the ravine and past the first few pools, where the polished walls of the stream trench reveal a spectacularly dense packing of crinoid fossils in the limestone. Deeper pools again stall progress after about 50 m.

To continue further down the gorge is however possible for those prepared to get wet. Best equipment for this is a swimming costume and gym pumps – together with a warm summer day; the cold water of winter would be not only unpleasant but also dangerous due to the threat of exposure. The trip through the gorge is nearly 500 m long; it is only possible in the downstream direction and there is no escape up the sheer walls. Wading through increasingly deep water is soon necessary as the beck twists through cascades and plunge pools, between polished limestone walls just a few metres apart. As it cuts deeper into the rock it becomes narrower, and a few solutional openings in the walls liken the gorge to a cave passage without a roof – they are after all both cut by fast-flowing streams.

After about 150 m there are three cascades each nearly 2 m high. The lower two are easy climbs but the smooth vertical wall of the top one is not. This is why the gorge descent is a one-way trip. The only way down is to jump into the plunge pool, which is quite deep enough, and swim a few strokes to the far side – which is just the narrow lip to the next cascade. This is where the gorge takes on an atmosphere inconceivable for anyone on the rim. The dark limestone walls are deeply undercut in deep swirl pockets; at one point the beck swings underneath a rock bridge and even the dry route over the bridge returns to another deep pool. The streambed is rarely less than 2 m wide, but higher up the walls close in to only a metre, and the darkness is intensified as they rise unbroken more than 15 m. After 100 m of this impressively narrow canyon, the walls part a little around the last two deep pools separated by an easily climbed cascade in a narrow slot. High above, the old bridge spans the daylight, and this is the sign that the gorge's gradient eases off towards its lower end.

Seen from the fellside, Hell Gill is just another narrow gorge of the type so often found in limestone, but its depth can hardly be

The bottom end of the Hell Gill gorge

guessed at. Seen from inside it is a whole new experience, and really provides the link between the surface streams and underground streams which between them fashion so much of the limestone landscape.

Public footpaths lead to and alongside the gorge, and provide access to both ends.

Index

35 – How Stean Gorge   093735

In its upper reaches, Nidderdale is a sombre valley, lined with dark woods and rugged crags of sandstone, and sadly lacking the white scars of limestone country. The reservoirs reflect a little light into the dale; Gouthwaite is perhaps best known for the marshes which appear when the water is low and create a paradise for bird-watchers. At the village of Lofthouse, the dale road divides. One road escapes east over the bleak moors to Masham, and the private road continues to the upper reservoirs. Westward the old packhorse route to Wharfedale is no more, and the tarmac ends at the tiny hamlet of Middlesmoor with its mediaeval church. Another road goes to Stean.

How Stean Beck is a major tributary to the Nidd, and it has found its way down to the main dale just where an outcrop of limestone forms the floor. A fault in the sequence of rocks has left the limestone band just a little higher here, so that erosion of the dale has exposed it surrounded by the overlying sandstone. The gently dipping, thin bedded limestone does have a cave system within it, but most of the flow of How Stean Beck has found it easier to stay on the surface and flow through a narrow gorge for just over a kilometre.

The gorge is approached by a very narrow lane connecting Lofthouse and Stean. Where the beck is crossed by the first bridge it is in a rocky ravine only a few metres deep. It comes as a surprise when the next bridge, between the café and the car park, crosses the gorge, some 15 m above the water. A footpath follows ledges through the deepest section of the gorge, and it starts from just beside the road bridge. Upstream the path follows the rim of the gorge. Depending on the weather, there is below either a tumbling torrent, or a sliver of silent water sliding over the limestone bed. The walls are carved into ledges and overhangs which follow the limestone bedding, and a few large blocks down in the water are testimony to ledges too deeply undercut. And look out for the moulins – rounded streambed potholes scoured by the water and one of the major ways by which a river deepens its bed.

A wider rock platform marks the top end of the path. Upstream